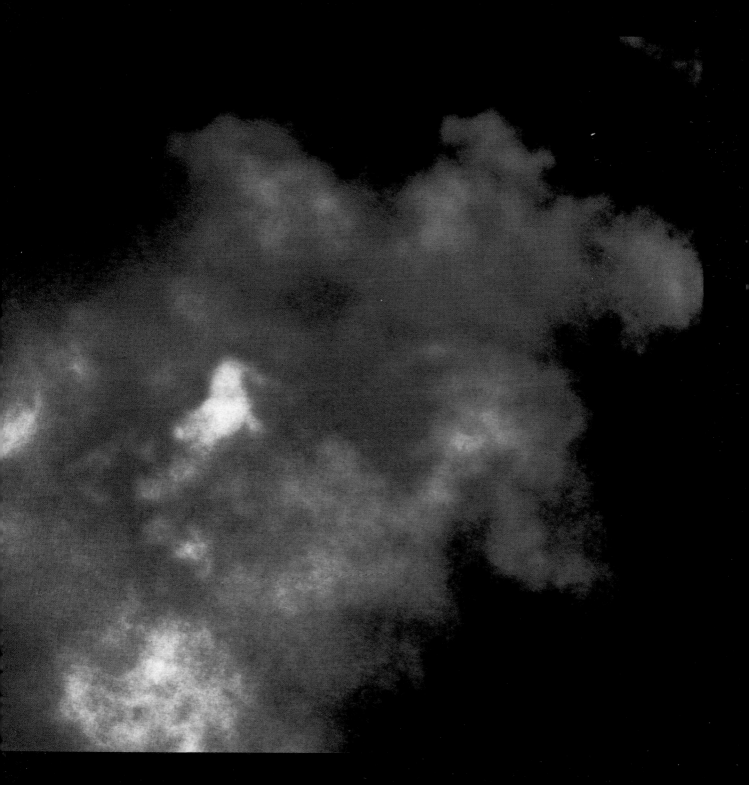

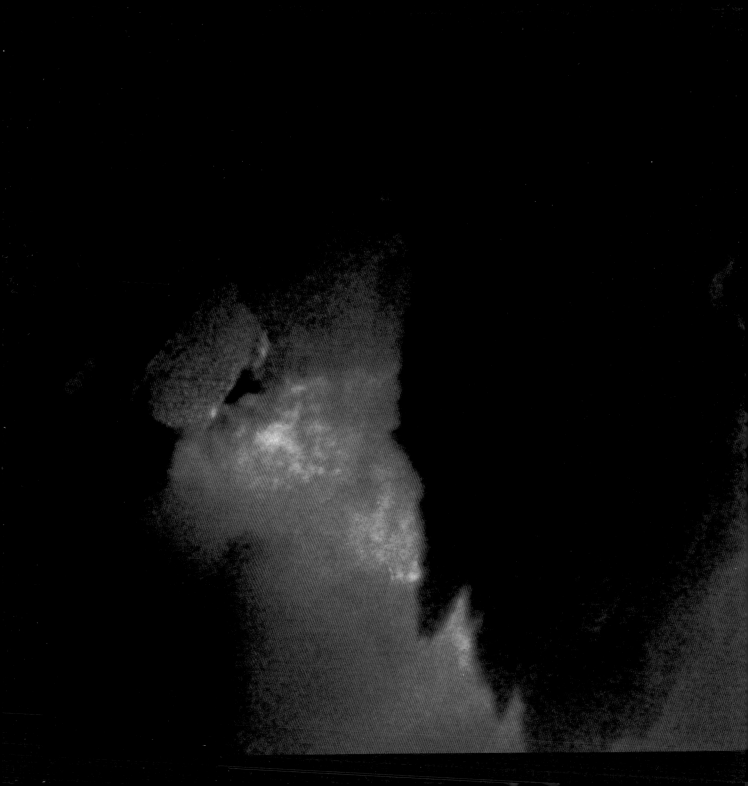

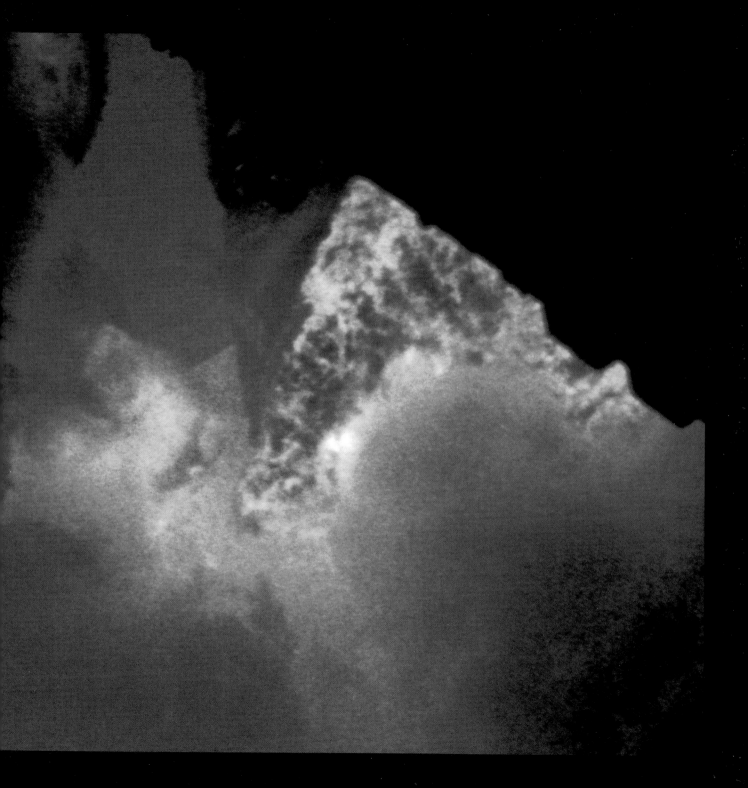

FULL MOON

MICHAEL LIGHT

EDWIN E. ALDRIN, JR.	CHARLES CONRAD, JR.
NEIL A. ARMSTRONG	CHARLES M. DUKE, JR.
WILLIAM A. ANDERS	R. WALTER CUNNINGHAM
ALAN L. BEAN	DONN F. EISELE
FRANK BORMAN	RONALD E. EVANS
EUGENE A. CERNAN	RICHARD F. GORDON, JR.
ROGER B. CHAFFEE	VIRGIL I. GRISSOM
MICHAEL COLLINS	FRED W. HAISE, JR.

APOLLO 1   APOLLO 7   APOLLO 8   APOLLO 9   APOLLO 10   APOLLO 11

JAMES B. IRWIN   RUSSELL L. SCHWEICKART

JAMES A. LOVELL, JR.   DAVID R. SCOTT

T. KENNETH MATTINGLY II   ALAN B. SHEPARD, JR.

JAMES A. McDIVITT   THOMAS P. STAFFORD

EDGAR D. MITCHELL   JOHN L. SWIGERT, JR.

STUART A. ROOSA   EDWARD H. WHITE II

WALTER M. SCHIRRA, JR.   ALFRED M. WORDEN

HARRISON H. SCHMITT   JOHN W. YOUNG

APOLLO 12   APOLLO 13   APOLLO 14   APOLLO 15   APOLLO 16   APOLLO 17

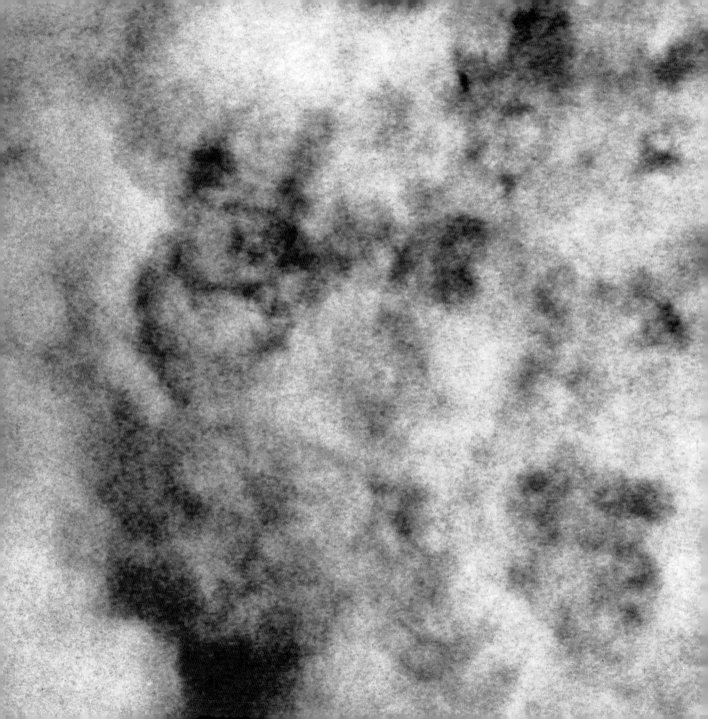

I

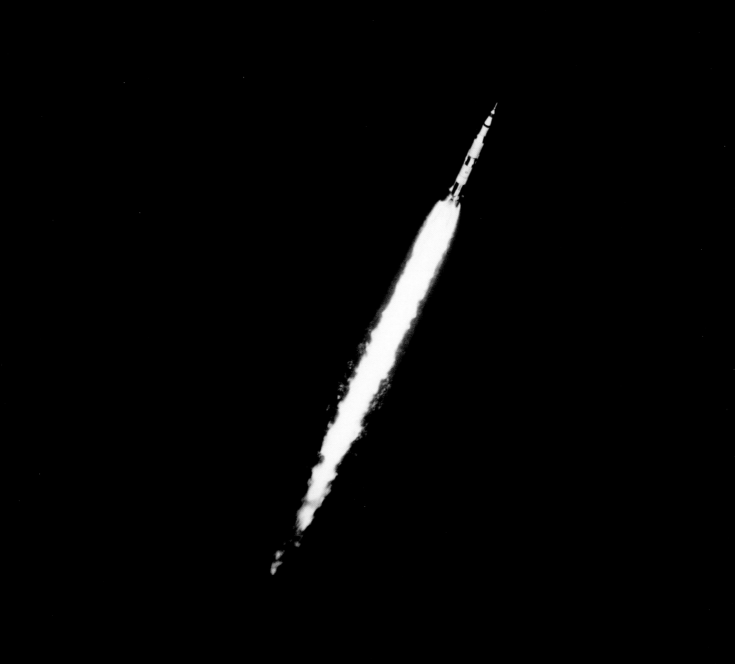

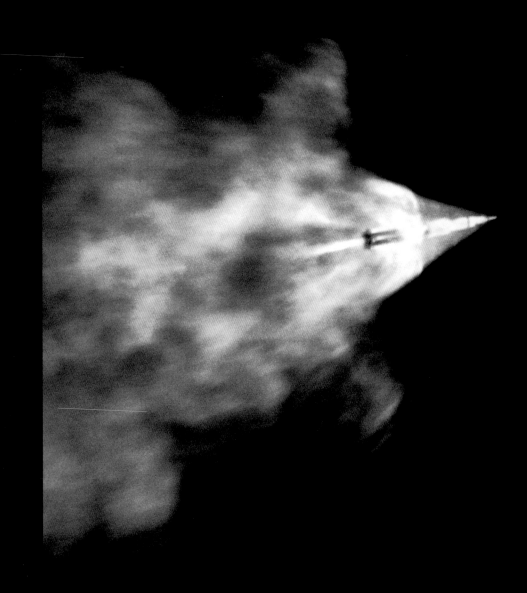

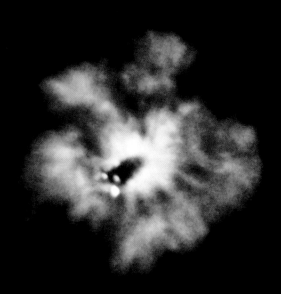

3

6

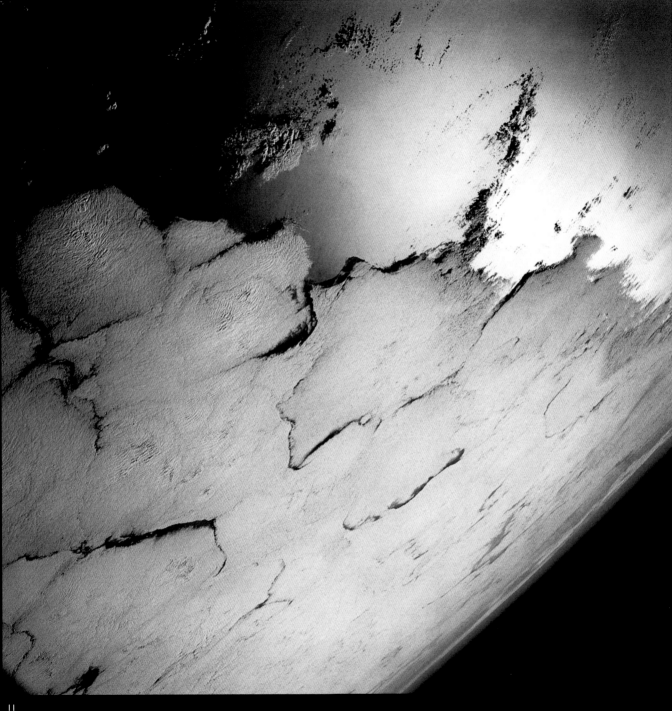

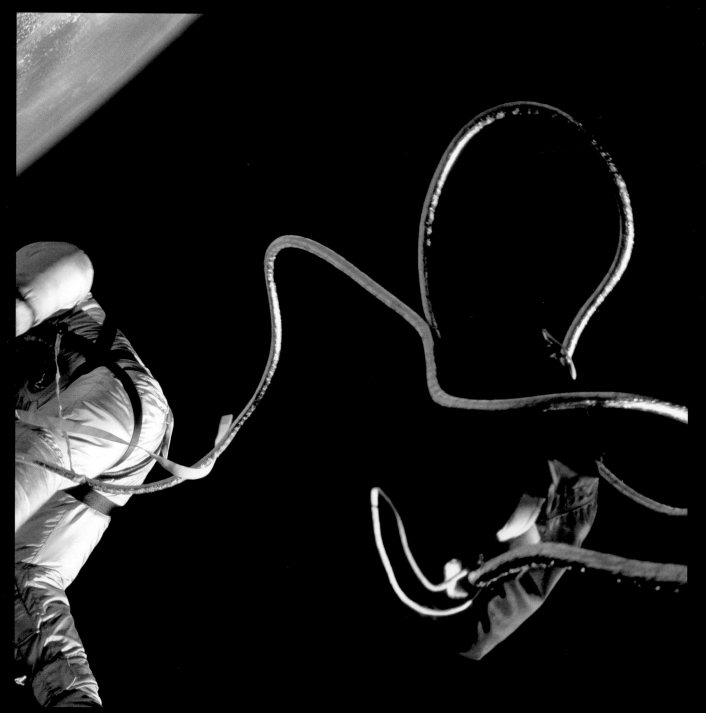

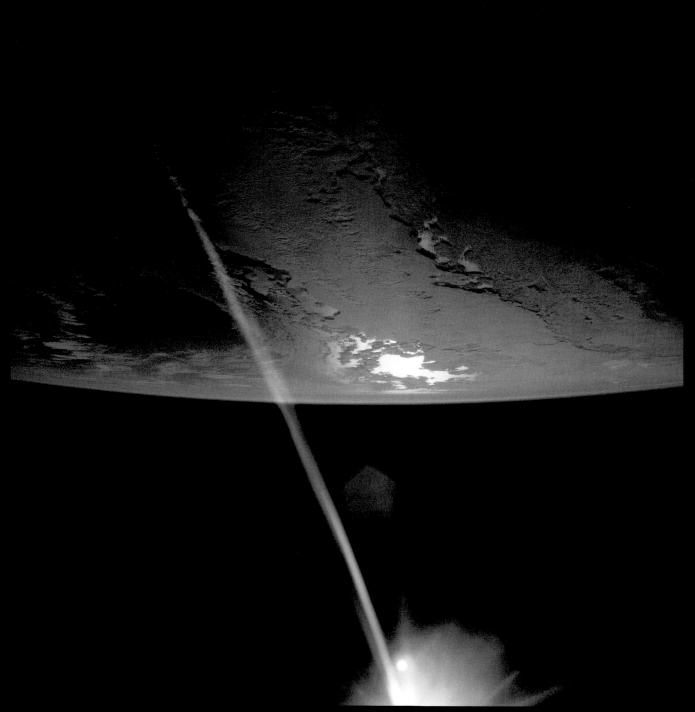

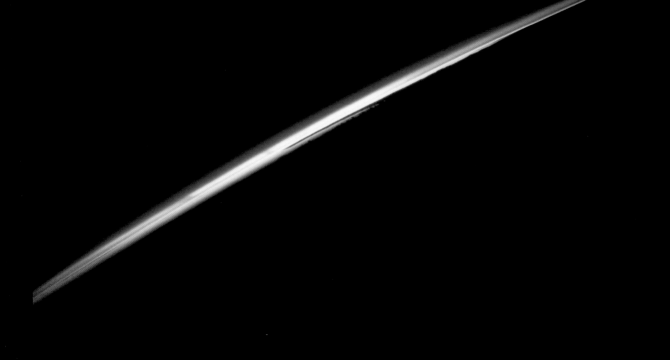

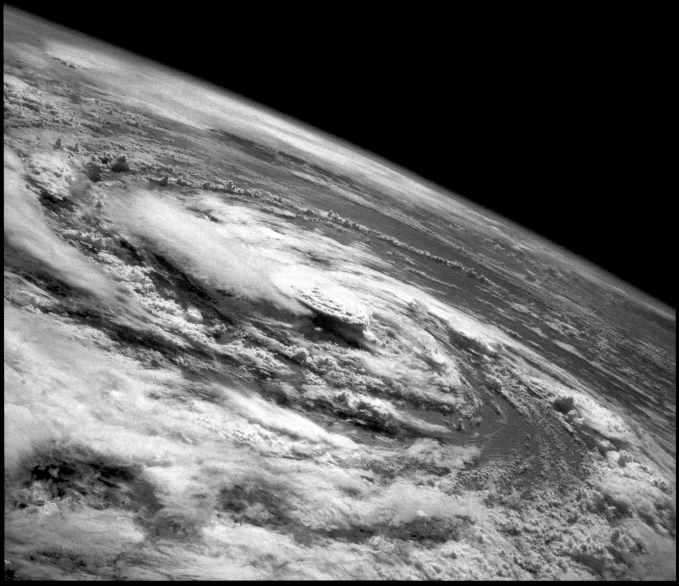

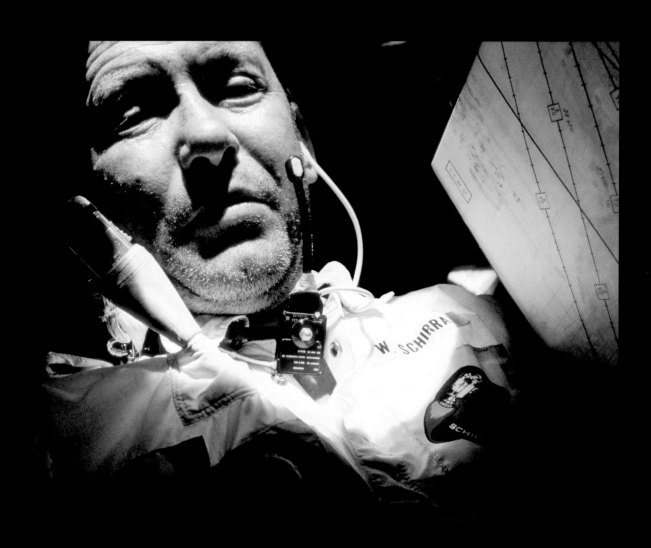

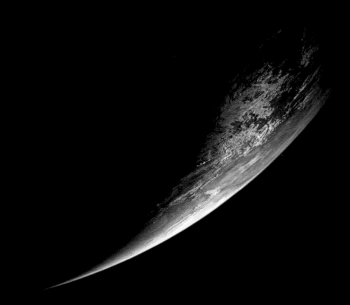

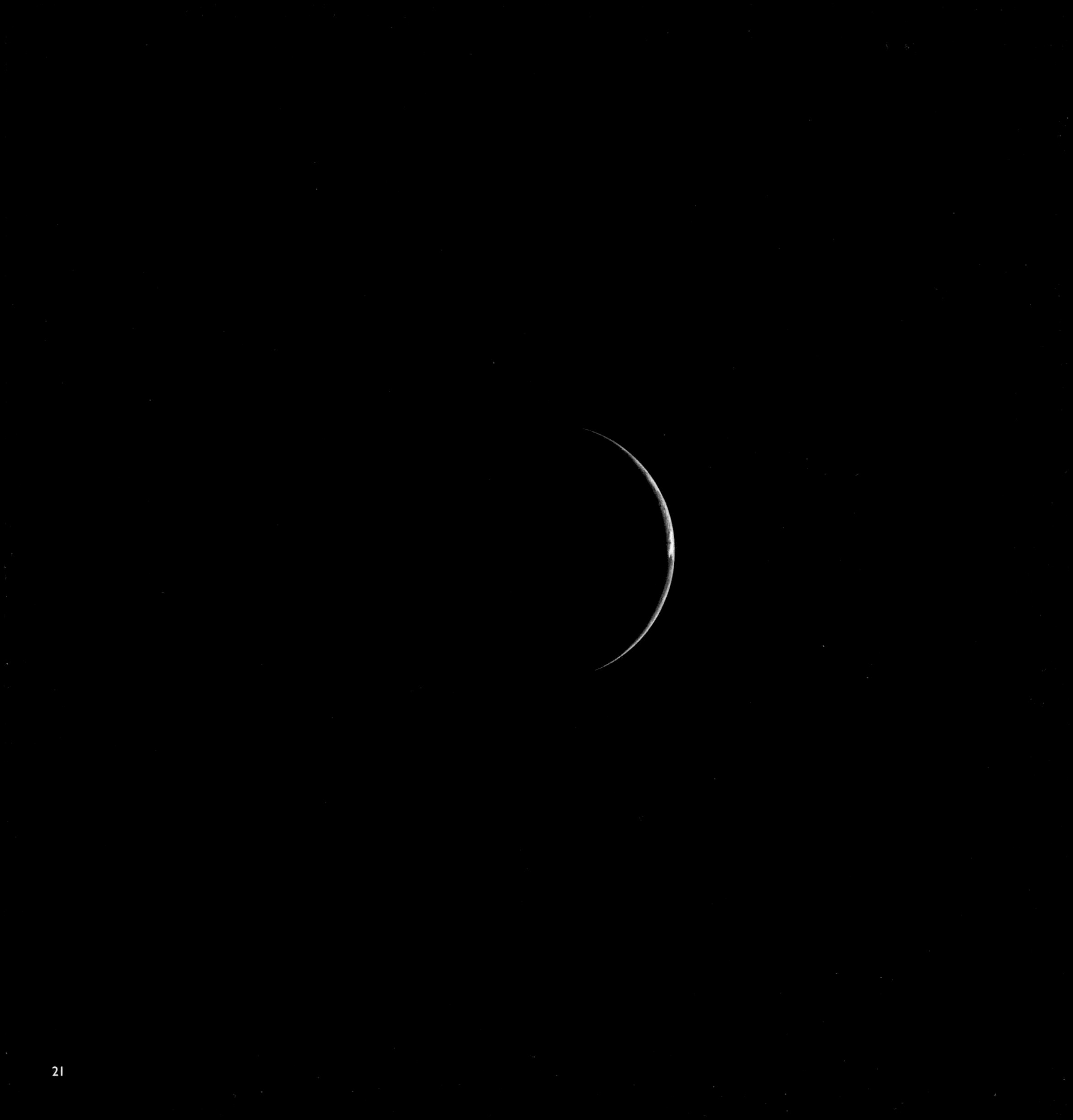

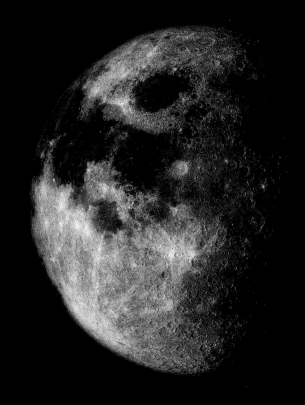

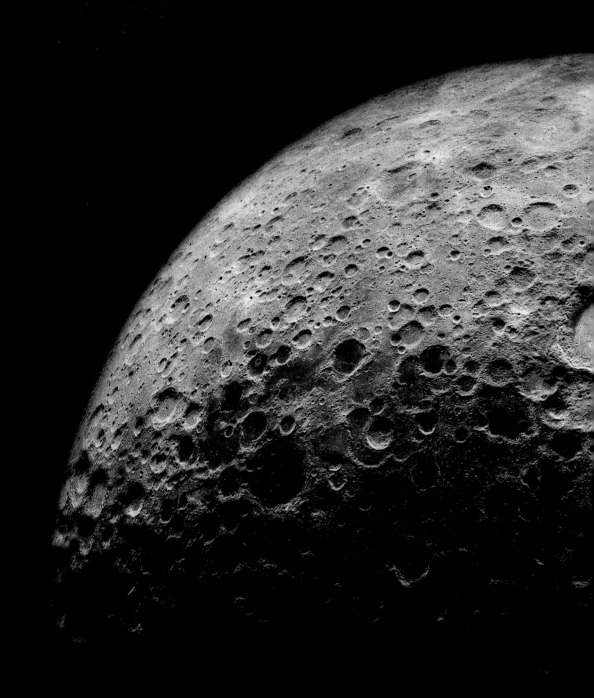

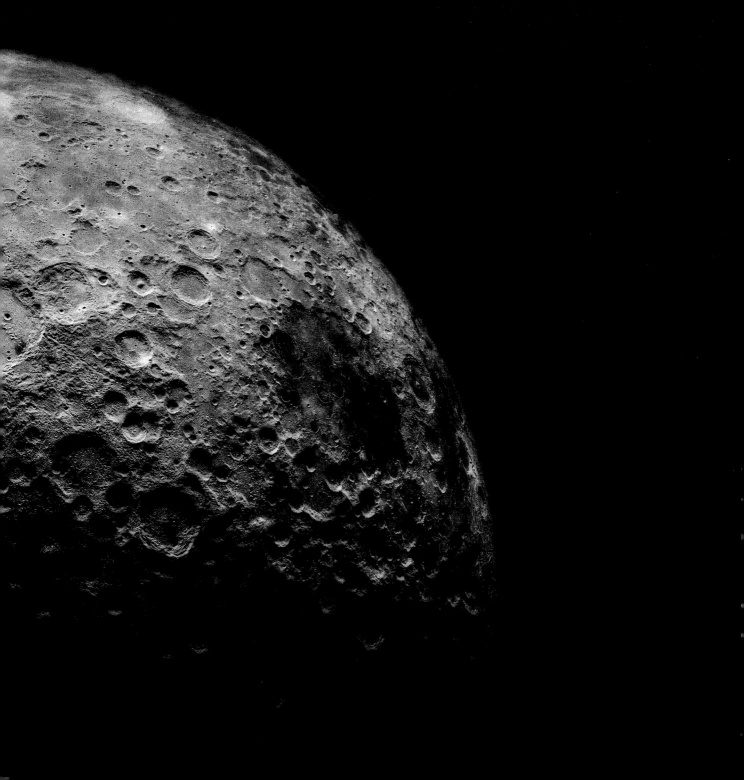

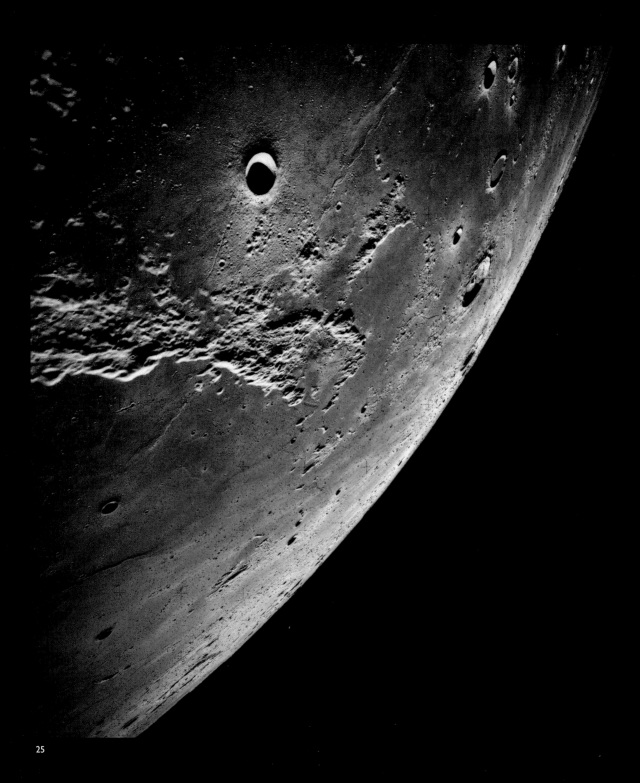

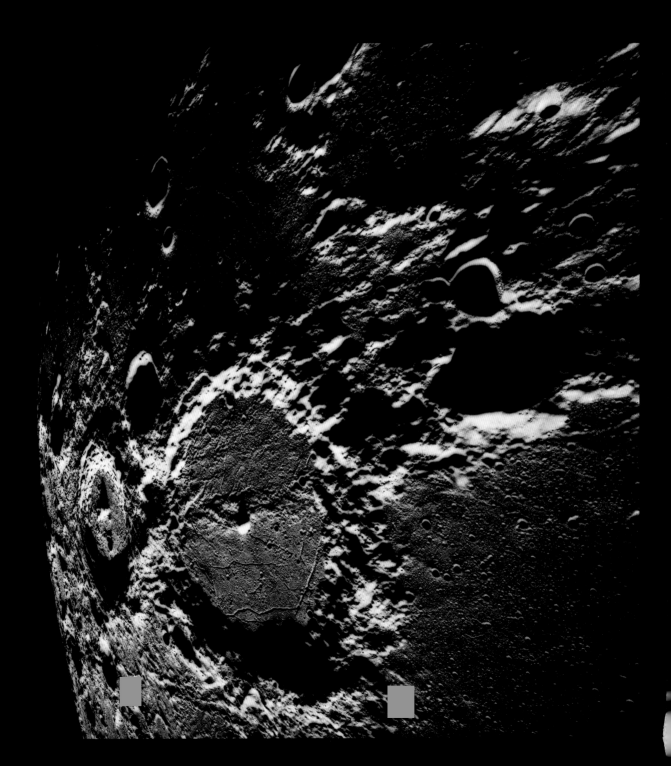

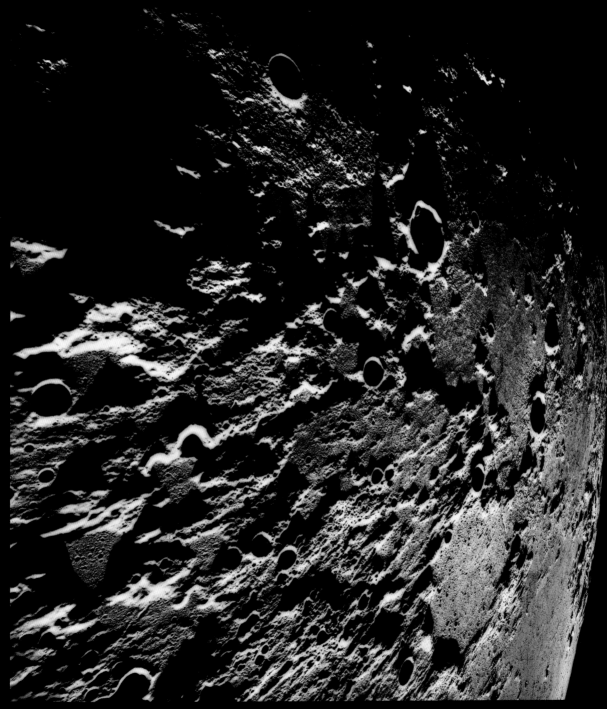

27

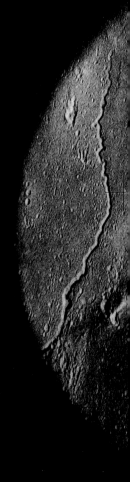

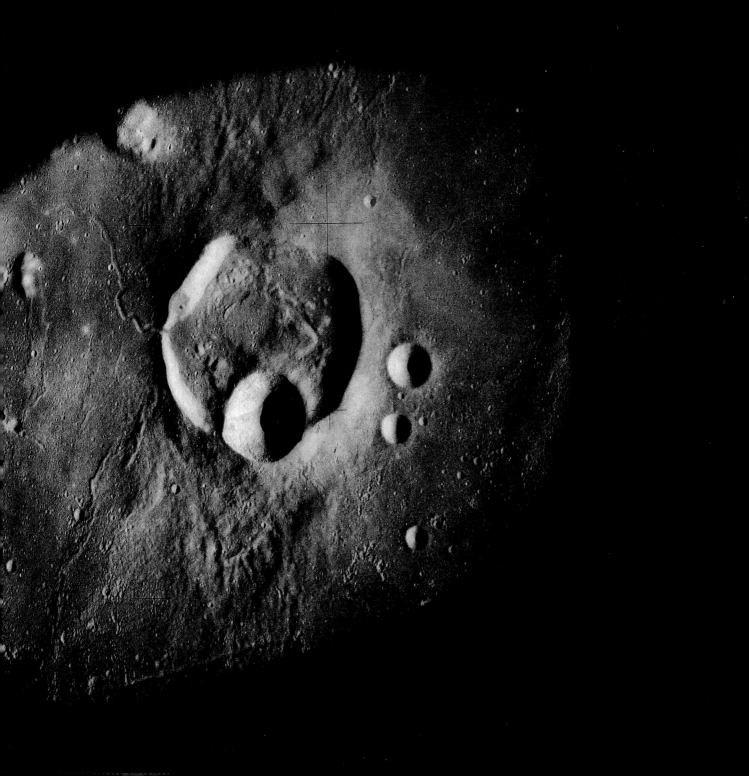

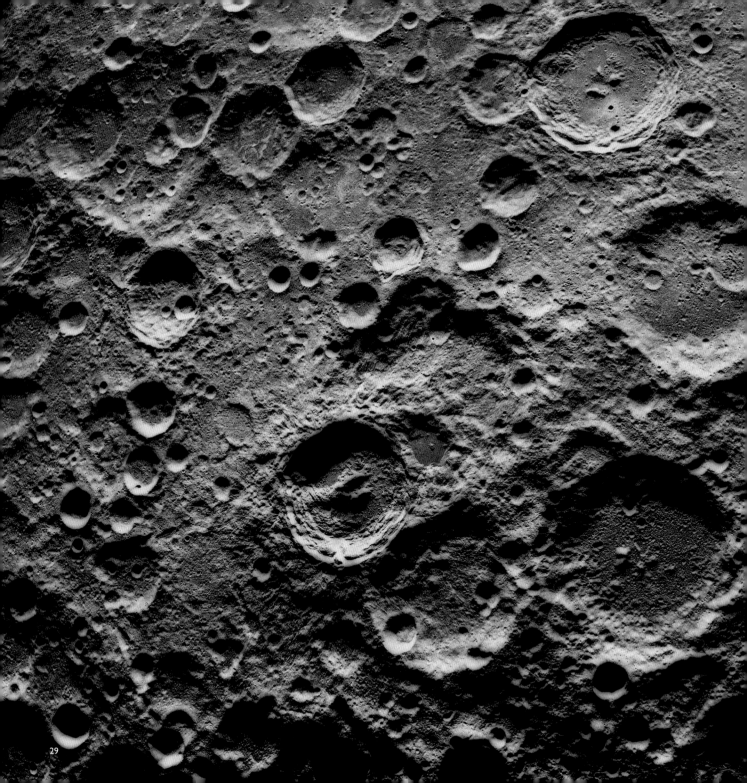

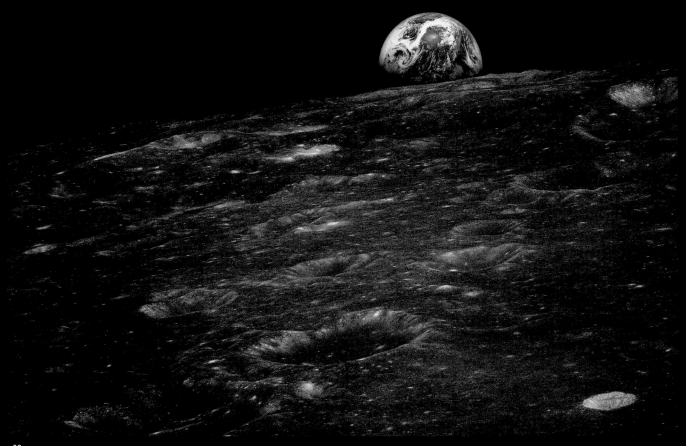

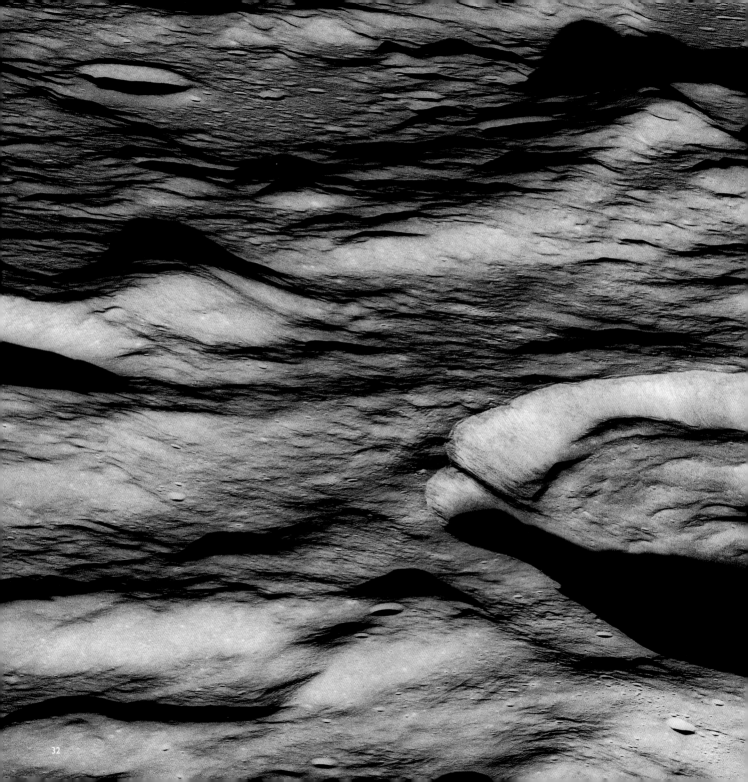

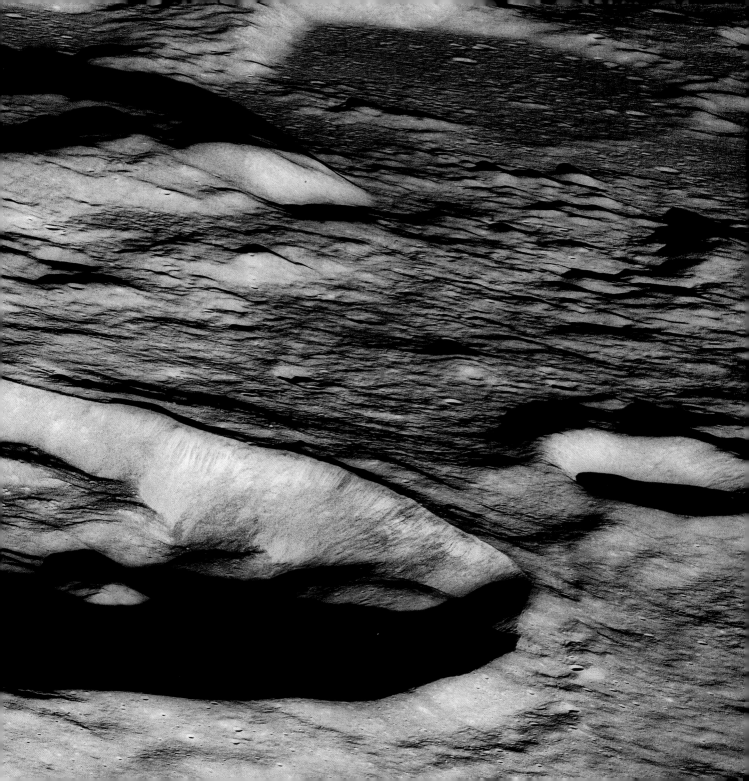

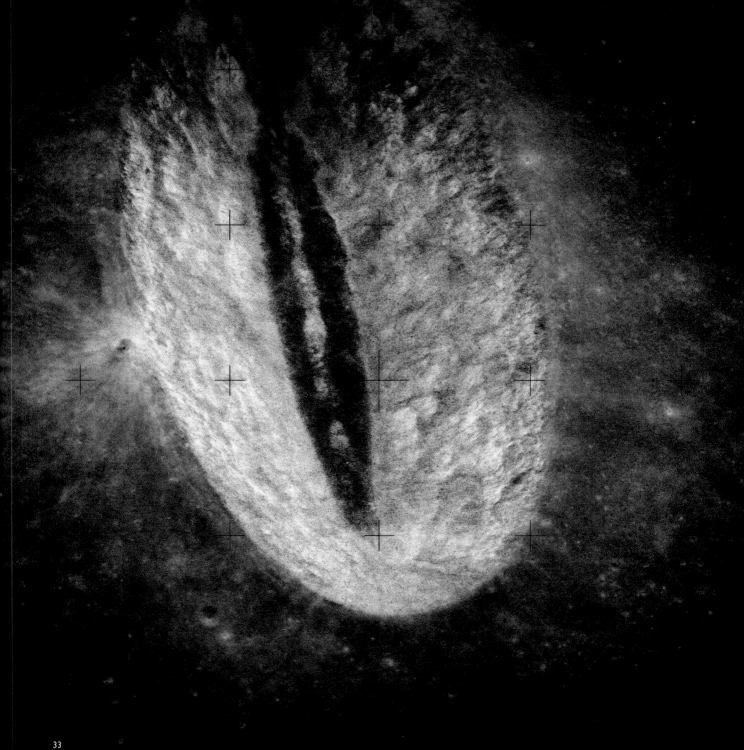

33

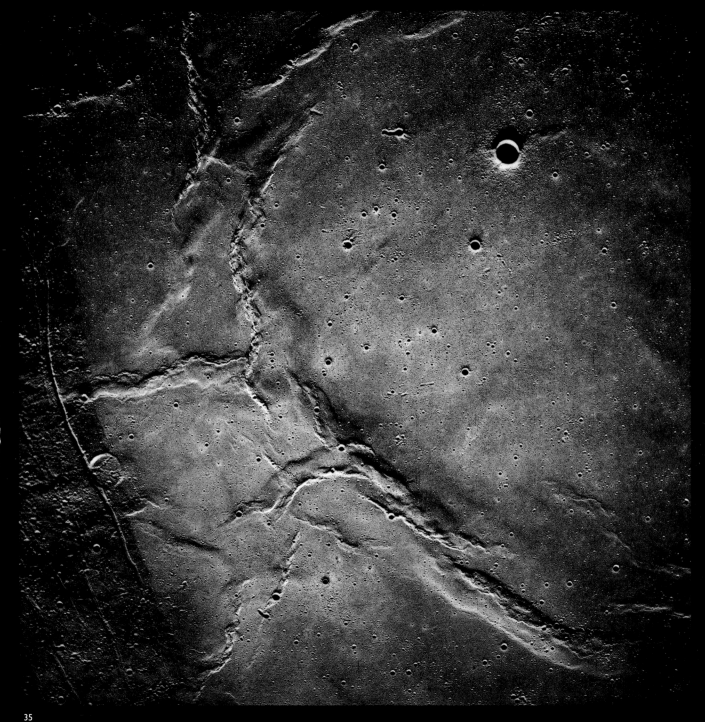

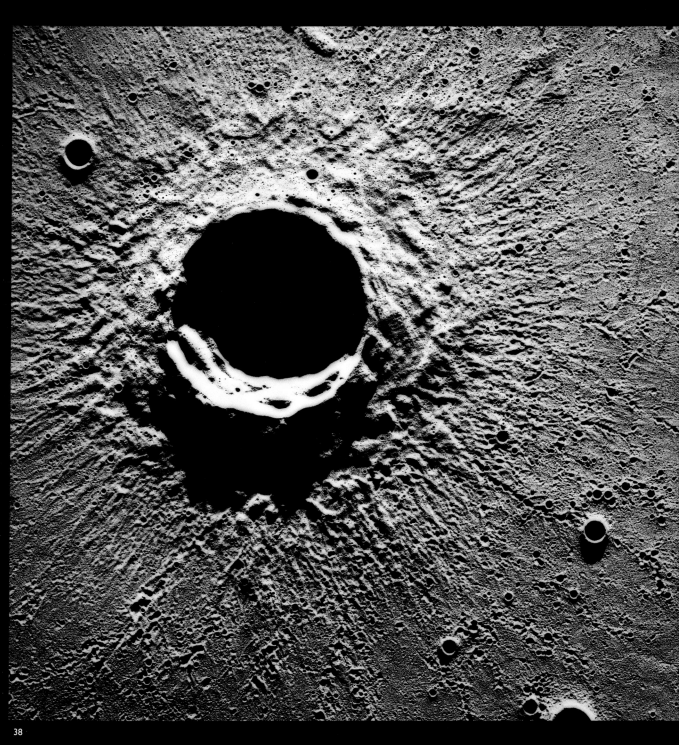

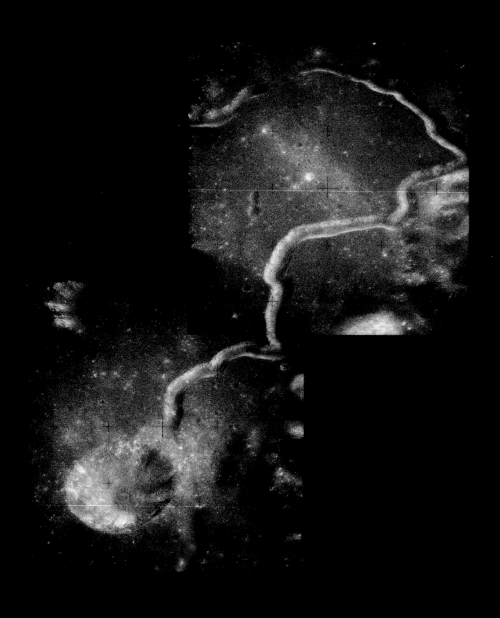

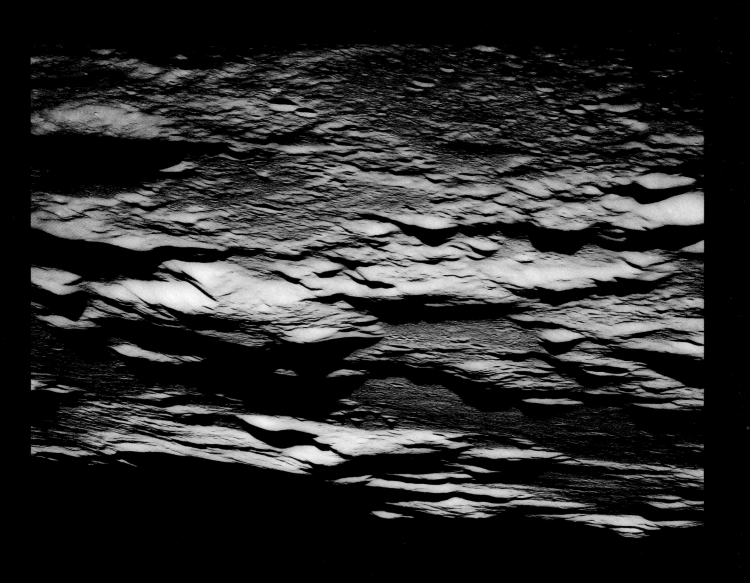

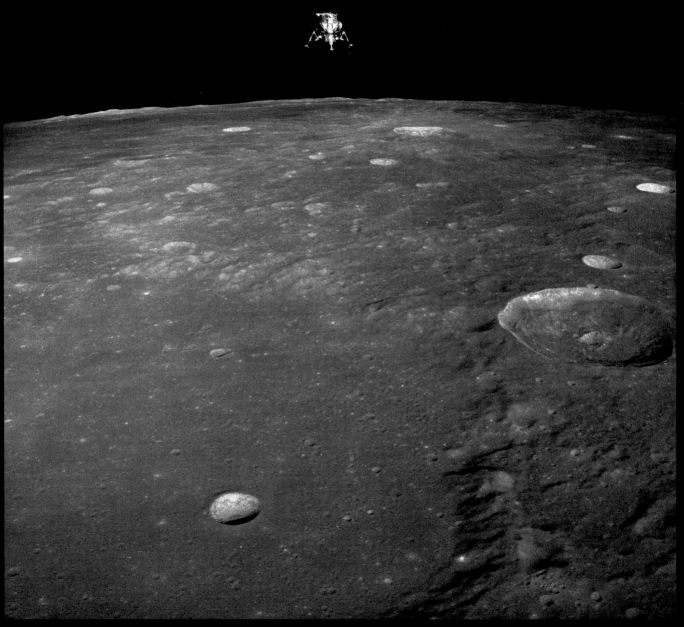

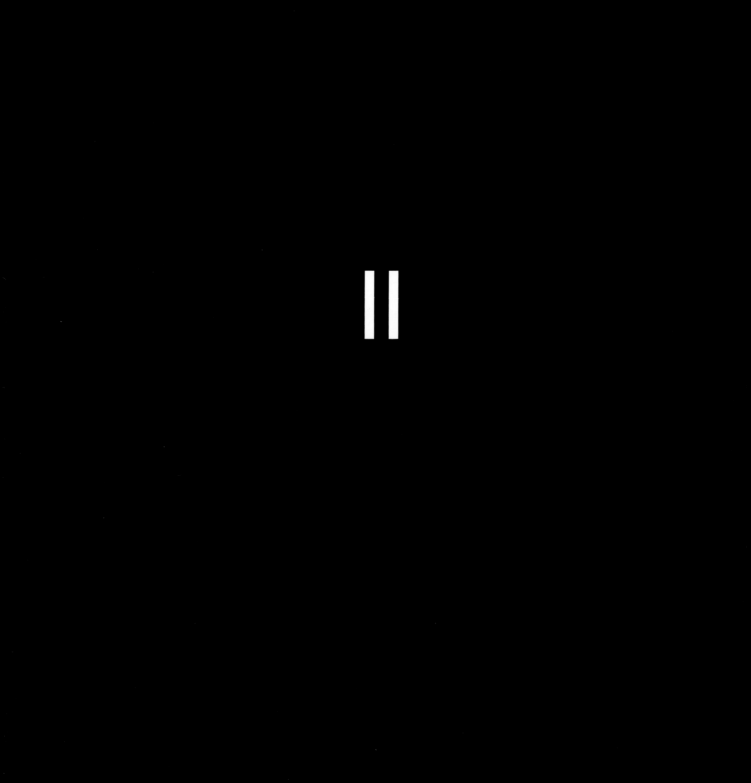

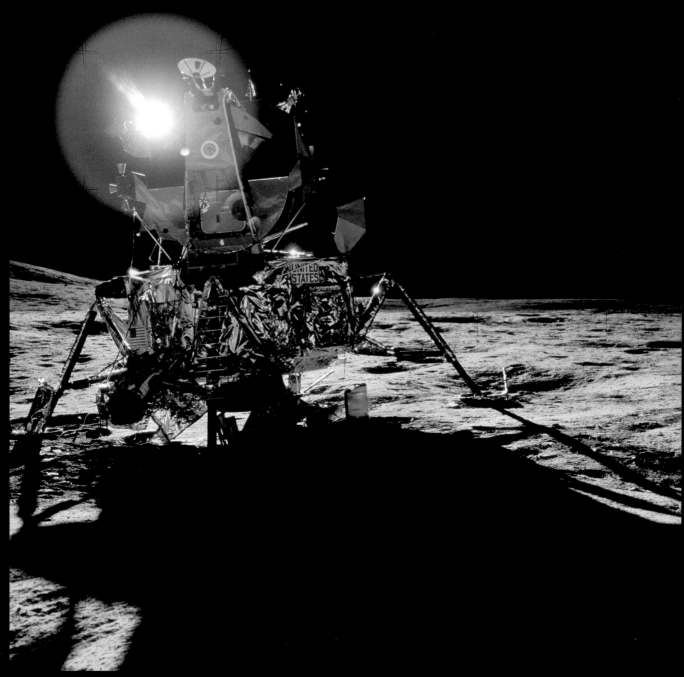

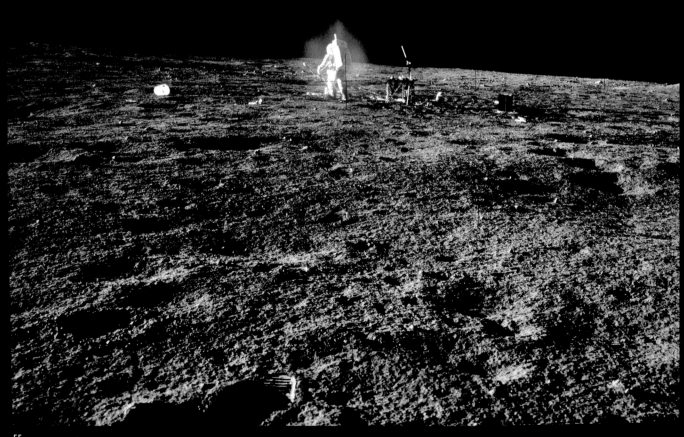

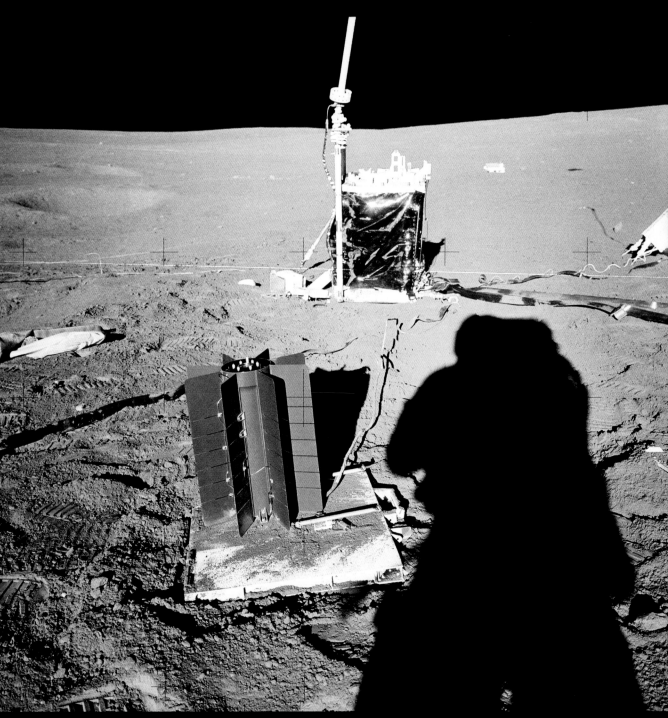

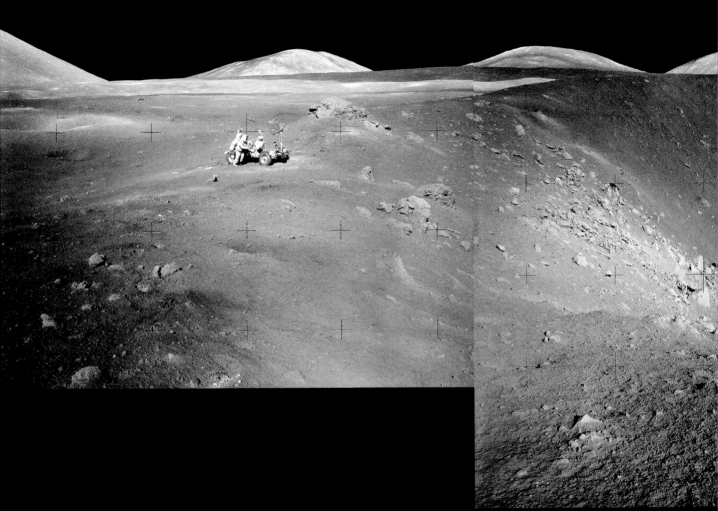

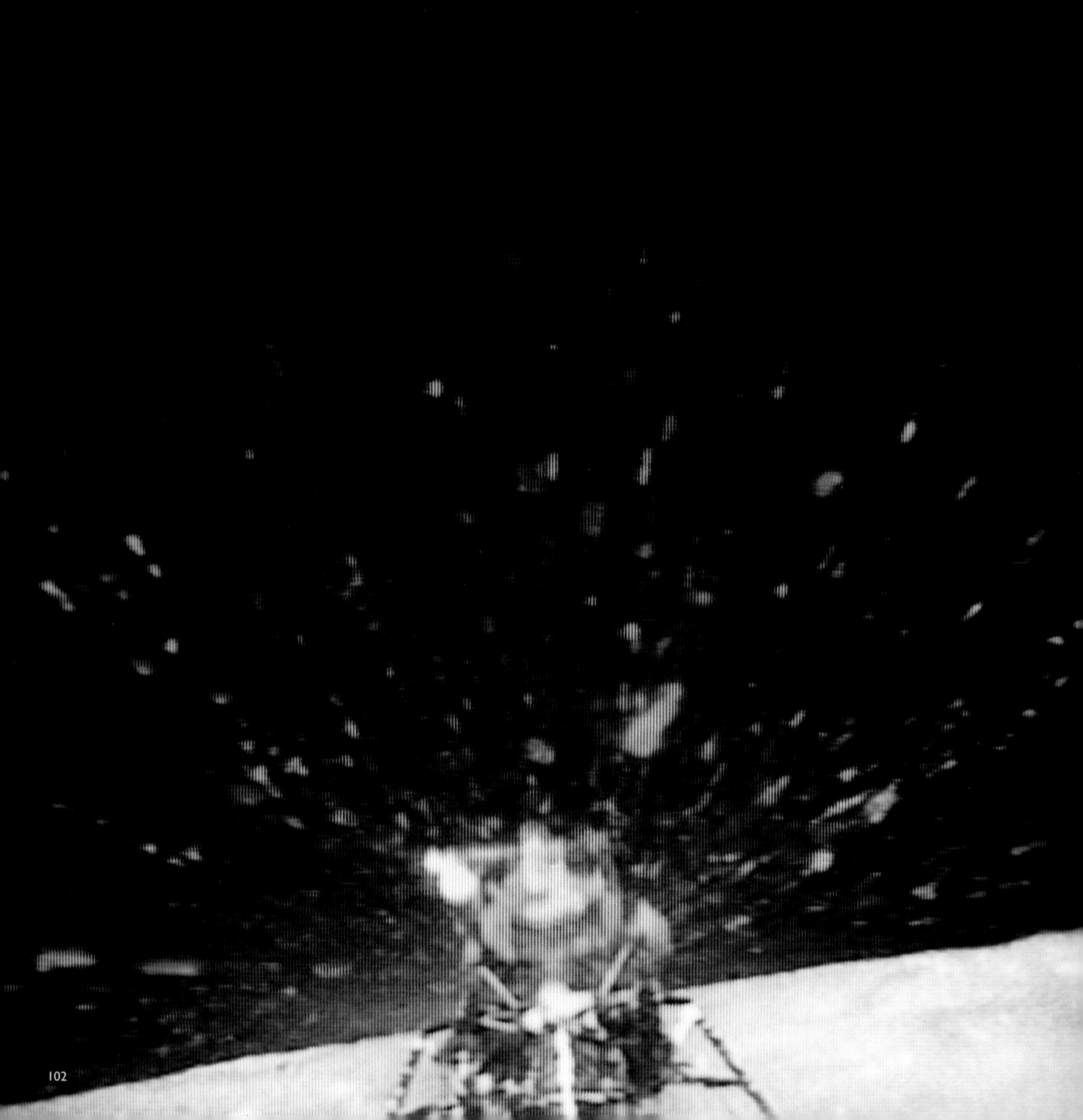

103

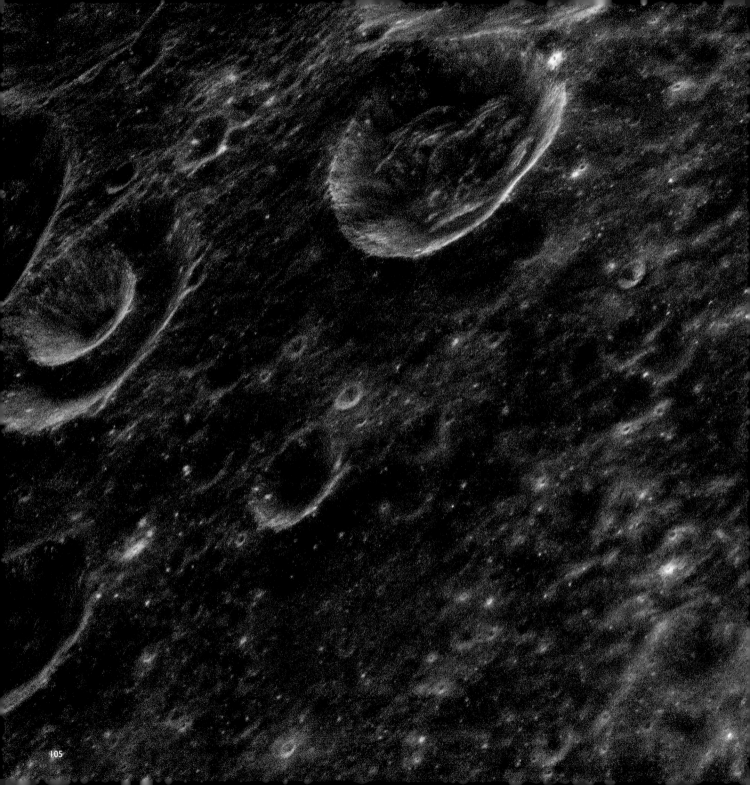

105

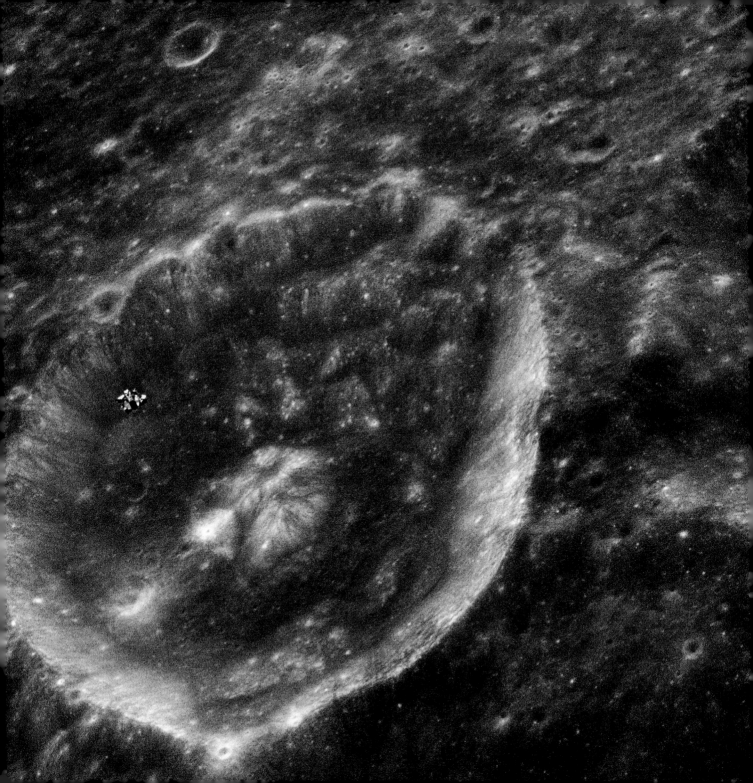

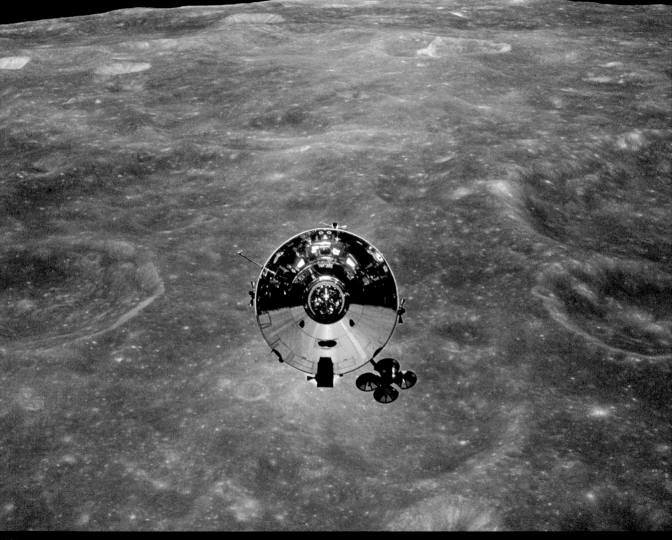

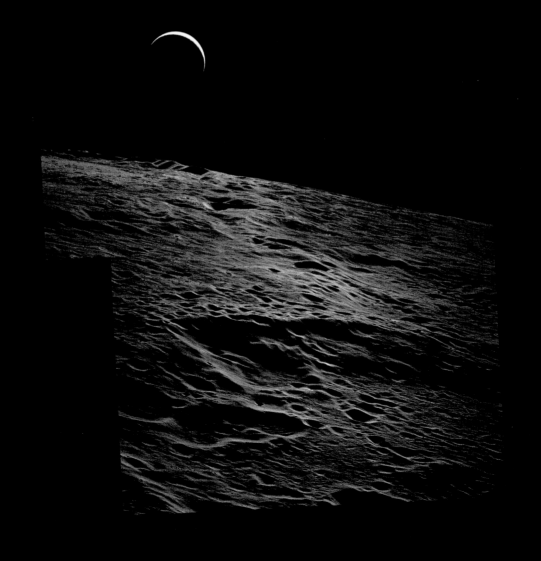

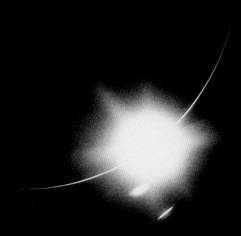

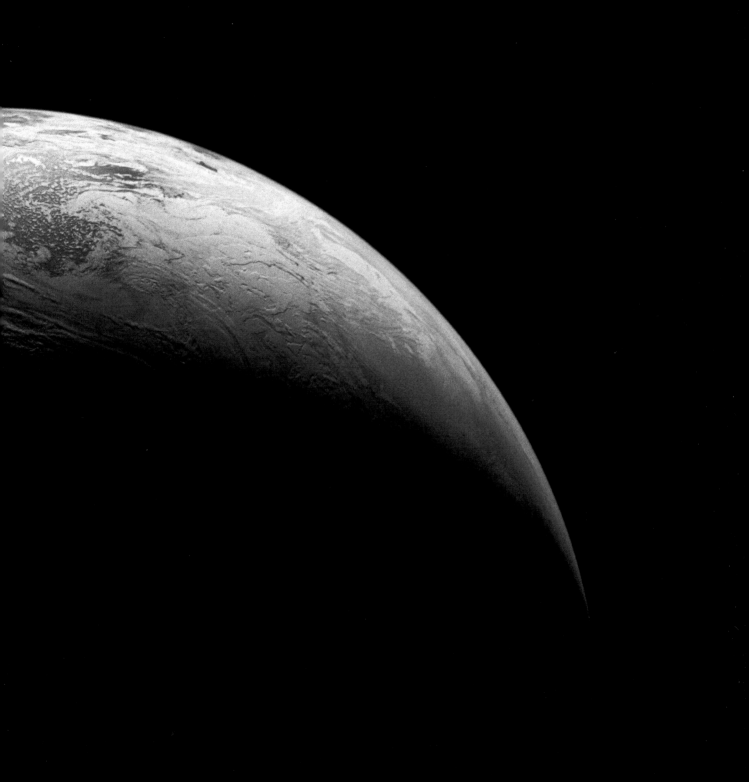

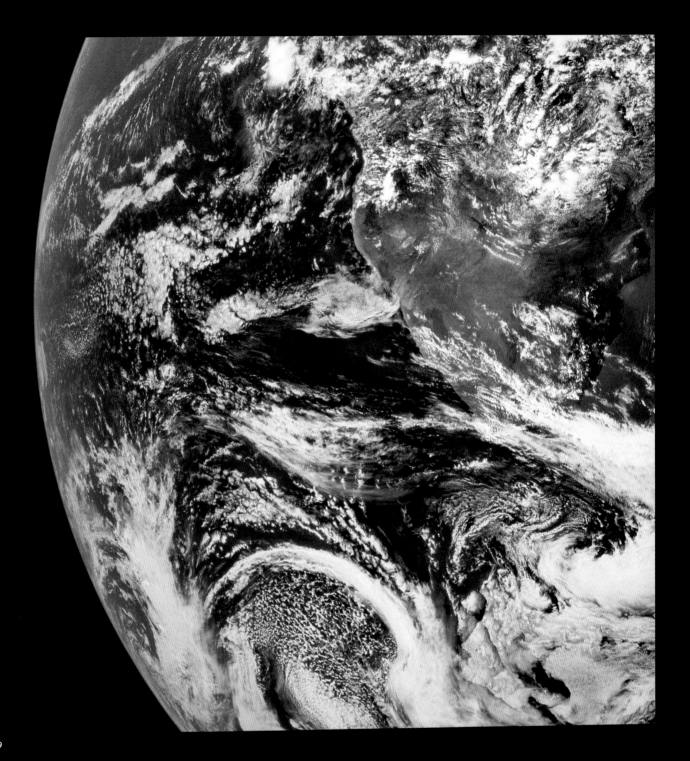

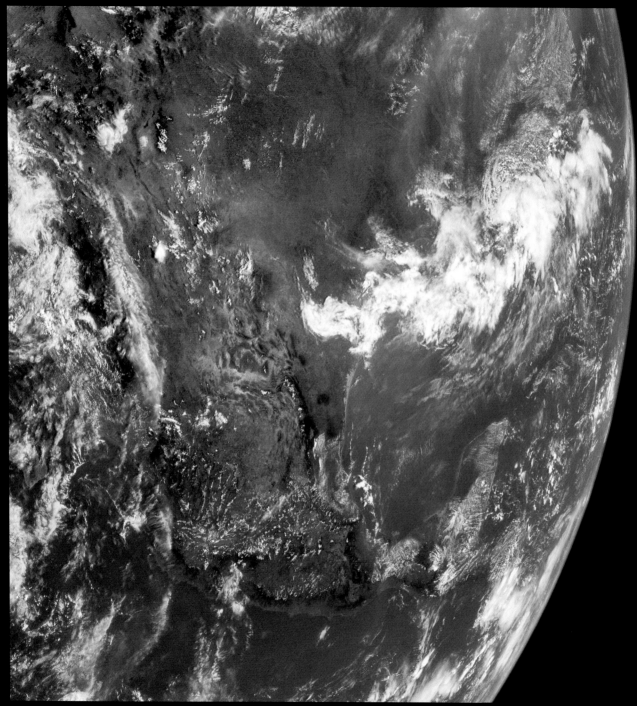

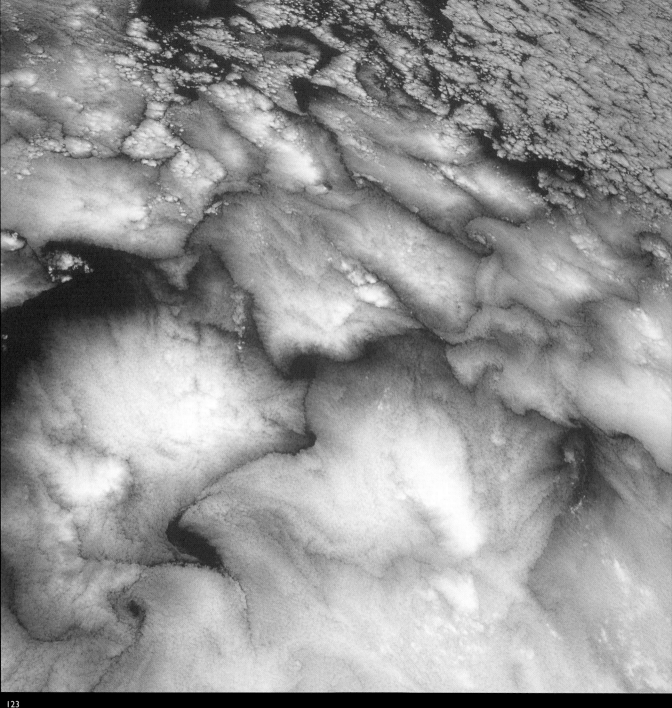

APOLLO MISSION DATA

Apollo 1: January 27, 1967
Crew: Commander (CDR) Virgil I. Grissom, Command Module Pilot (CMP) Edward H. White II, Lunar Module Pilot (LMP) Roger B. Chaffee
Description: Crew perished tragically in cockpit fire during pre-launch ground test.

Apollo 7: October 11–22, 1968
Crew: CDR Walter M. Schirra, Jr., CMP Donn F. Eisele, LMP R. Walter Cunningham
Description: 1st manned test of command and service modules, 163 Earth orbits.
Mission duration: 10 days, 20 hrs, 9 min

Apollo 8: December 21–27, 1968
Crew: CDR Frank Borman, CMP James A. Lovell, Jr., LMP William A. Anders
Description: 1st manned flight around Moon; 10 orbits on Christmas Eve, 1968.
Time in lunar orbit: 20 hrs, 7 min
Mission duration: 6 days, 3 hrs, 1 min

Apollo 9: March 3–13, 1969
Crew: CDR James A. McDivitt, CMP David R. Scott, LMP Russell L. Schweickart
Description: Earth-orbit test of the entire Apollo spacecraft. Included rendezvous between command module and lunar module; 38-minute space walk.
Spacecraft (command module, lunar module): *Gumdrop, Spider*
Mission duration: 10 days, 1 hr, 1 min

Apollo 10: May 18–26, 1969
Crew: CDR Thomas P. Stafford, CMP John W. Young, LMP Eugene A. Cernan
Description: Rehearsal for landing; lunar module descended to 50,000 feet above Moon.
Spacecraft (command module, lunar module): *Charlie Brown, Snoopy*
Time in lunar orbit: 2 days, 13 hrs, 41 min
Mission duration: 8 days, 0 hrs, 3 min

Apollo 11: July 16–24, 1969
Crew: CDR Neil A. Armstrong, CMP Michael Collins, LMP Edwin E. Aldrin, Jr.
Description: 1st lunar landing.
Spacecraft (command module, lunar module): *Columbia, Eagle*
Time in lunar orbit: 2 days, 11 hrs, 34 min
Lunar landing date, location: July 20, Sea of Tranquillity
Time on lunar surface: 21 hrs, 36 min
Moonwalk duration: 2 hrs, 31 min
Pounds of samples collected: 47.7
Mission duration: 8 days, 3 hrs, 18 min

Apollo 12: November 14–24, 1969
Crew: CDR Charles Conrad, Jr., CMP Richard F. Gordon, Jr., LMP Alan L. Bean
Description: 2nd lunar landing; 600 feet from unmanned Surveyor 3 probe.
Spacecraft (command module, lunar module): *Yankee Clipper, Intrepid*
Time in lunar orbit: 3 days, 17 hrs, 2 min
Lunar landing date, location: November 19, Ocean of Storms
Time on lunar surface: 1 day, 7 hrs, 31 min
Moonwalk durations: 1st: 3 hrs, 56 min; 2nd: 3 hrs, 49 min
Pounds of samples collected: 75.7
Mission duration: 10 days, 4 hrs, 36 min

Apollo 13: April 11–17, 1970
Crew: CDR James A. Lovell, Jr., CMP John L. Swigert, Jr., LMP Fred W. Haise, Jr.
Description: 3rd landing attempt; aborted following explosion of oxygen tank inside service module; classified as a "successful failure" because of crew rescue.
Spacecraft (command module, lunar module): *Odyssey, Aquarius*
Mission duration: 5 days, 22 hrs, 54 min

Apollo 14: January 31–February 9, 1971
Crew: CDR Alan B. Shepard, Jr., CMP Stuart A. Roosa, LMP Edgar D. Mitchell
Description: 3rd landing, 1st mission devoted entirely to scientific exploration.
Spacecraft (command module, lunar module): *Kitty Hawk, Antares*
Time in lunar orbit: 2 days, 18 hrs, 40 min
Lunar landing date, location: February 5, Fra Mauro Highlands
Time on lunar surface: 1 day, 9 hrs, 30 min
Moonwalk durations: 1st: 4 hrs, 47 min; 2nd: 4 hrs, 34 min
Pounds of samples collected: 94.4
MIssion duration: 9 days, 0 hrs, 2 min

Apollo 15: July 26–August 7, 1971
Crew: CDR David R. Scott, CMP Alfred M. Worden, LMP James B. Irwin
Description: 4th landing, 1st "J-mission" expedition, featuring extended lunar stay time, long-duration backpacks, and the electric, 4-wheel-drive lunar rover car.
Spacecraft (command module, lunar module): *Endeavor, Falcon*
Time in lunar orbit: 6 days, 1 hr, 17 min
Lunar landing date, location: July 30, Hadley–Apennine Plains
Time on lunar surface: 2 days, 18 hrs, 54 min
Moonwalk durations: 1st: 6 hrs, 32 min; 2nd: 7 hrs, 12 min; 3rd: 4 hrs, 49 min
Pounds of samples collected: 169
Mission duration: 12 days, 7 hrs, 12 min

Apollo 16: April 16–27, 1972
Crew: CDR John W. Young, CMP T. Kenneth Mattingly II, LMP Charles M. Duke, Jr.
Description: 5th landing; exploration of the Moon's central highlands.
Spacecraft (command module, lunar module): *Casper, Orion*
Time in lunar orbit: 5 days, 5 hrs, 53 min
Lunar landing date, location: April 20, Descartes Highlands
Time on lunar surface: 2 days, 23 hrs, 2 min
Moonwalk durations: 1st: 7 hrs, 11 min; 2nd: 7 hrs, 23 min; 3rd: 5 hrs, 40 min
Pounds of samples collected: 208.3
Mission duration: 11 days, 1 hr, 51 min

Apollo 17: December 7–19, 1972
Crew: CDR Eugene A. Cernan, CMP Ronald E. Evans, LMP Harrison H. Schmitt
Description: 6th and final landing. Schmitt was first scientist on the Moon.
Spacecraft (command module, lunar module): *America, Challenger*
Time in lunar orbit: 6 days, 3 hrs, 48 min
Lunar landing date, location: December 11, Taurus-Littrow Valley
Time on lunar surface: 3 days, 2 hrs, 59 min
Moonwalk durations: 1st: 7 hrs, 11 min; 2nd: 7 hrs, 36 min; 3rd: 7 hrs, 15 min
Pounds of samples collected: 243.1
Mission duration: 12 days, 13 hrs, 51 min

(Source: Chaikin, **A Man On The Moon**)

4.

20.

3.

2.

21.

22.

23.

1.

5.

6.

THERE ...

1. Saturn V rocket lifts off.
2. First stage separates; second stage ignites.
3. Second stage separates; third stage ignites.
4. Earth "parking" orbit.
5. Third stage reignites for "translunar injection."
6. Command Service Module (CSM) separates from third stage.
7. CSM docks with Lunar Module (LM); separates from third stage.
8. Midcourse trajectory correction, if required.
9. CSM engine slows spacecraft into lunar orbit.
10. Two astronauts move to LM, one remains CSM.
11. CSM and LM separate.
12. LM descent rocket fires.
13. Touchdown on lunar surface.

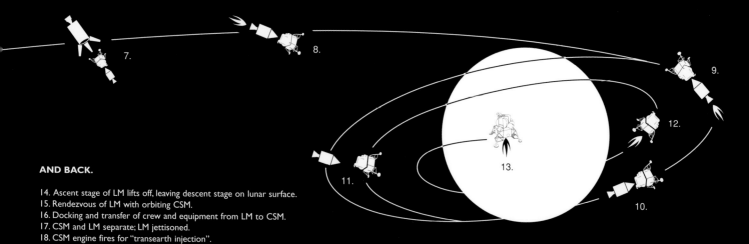

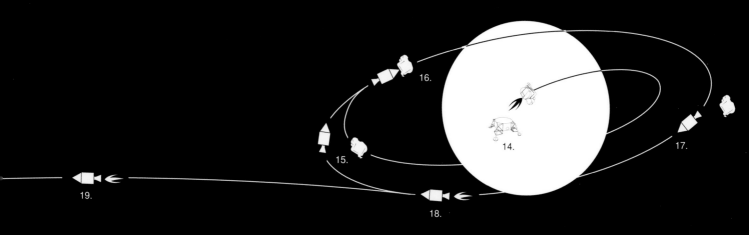

AND BACK.

14. Ascent stage of LM lifts off, leaving descent stage on lunar surface.
15. Rendezvous of LM with orbiting CSM.
16. Docking and transfer of crew and equipment from LM to CSM.
17. CSM and LM separate; LM jettisoned.
18. CSM engine fires for "transearth injection".
19. Midcourse trajectory correction, if required.
20. CM separates from SM; SM jettisoned.
21. Heat shield forward, CM reenters Earth atmosphere.
22. Parachutes deploy.
23. Splashdown in Pacific Ocean.

A NOTE ON THE PHOTOGRAPHS

Full Moon has used the latest in digital techniques to obtain the highest-quality photographic reproduction possible, resulting in a major advance over past NASA procedures for providing imagery to the public. When the Apollo missions returned to Earth, the Agency duplicated the fragile and precious original film once before putting it into cold storage. These "master dupes" were then used to make succeeding copies when an image request was received. In the past, the masters were never allowed out of NASA's possession, so publishers and exhibitors have had to make do with fourth- and fifth-generation duplicates, resulting in image deterioration and substantial loss of information with each succeeding generation.

By negotiating permission from NASA to take the masters offsite and digitally scan them at film resolution, *Full Moon* has circumvented this unfortunate procedure. The advent of digital imaging has made it possible to "clone" rather than "reproduce" an image, avoiding the addition of successive generations and thus keeping far more visual information intact. Application of digital technology at the source also allows subtle control of color balance, contrast, and density in ways that far surpass conventional analog darkroom techniques, as well as the ability to delicately composite separate images into panoramas.

Because of the scientific- and documentary-survey nature of the Apollo images, I have been especially careful in my use of powerful digital tools not to alter them beyond what any good printer might do in making a fine exhibition print. Naturally, even this required a host of aesthetic decisions for each image – for which I am solely responsible – but in each case I let the information on the film lead me, not vice versa. Color was the most demanding challenge. As explained in the essay in this book, the physics of human color-perception on the Moon are more complex and subjective than on Earth. Film itself adds its own peculiar characteristics to a recorded image, and the type of film and processing methods used also varied from mission to mission. Color accuracy is further complicated by the fact that in the process of duplication, NASA's masters often gained a blue, green, cyan, or yellow cast that simply is not present on the original film. My guide has been the fact that lunar soil, when held in the hand on the Moon's surface, appears as lighter and darker shades of gray.

In general, all images appear in the book as they were made on the missions. All black-and-white reproductions were shot on black-and-white negative film, all color reproductions on color transparency film. With the exception of certain double-page spreads and Earth images floating in black space, I have kept image cropping to a minimum, holding to full-frame reproduction as a matter of course. I have taken liberties with four images, however, in each case digitally removing certain small items for aesthetic reasons. In images 26 and 27, I have removed a thin sensor probe that intruded into the picture frame from the orbiting command module. In images 72 and 78, I have removed the reseau lens grid marks. Finally, I have added a slight, digitally induced blur to the enlargement of image 58, the family photograph on the surface of the Moon.

Regarding captions, I have checked and rechecked each to ensure the highest accuracy. Errors may remain, however, and I apologize for them in advance. Accurate attribution of inflight imagery to the particular astronaut who shot it is more difficult than with surface material because there are fewer hard records from which to reconstruct the sequence of events. In cases where doubts remain, I have given a "probably by" attribution to the mission's command module pilot, who was in general formally assigned most of a mission's inflight photographic duties by NASA.

For information on digitally-scanned and processed Apollo imagery, contact *www.projectfullmoon.com.*

128

THE SKIN OF THE MOON

Like most people alive between 1967 and 1972, I remember the Apollo missions. They began pretty dimly for me, at age four, but by the time Eugene Cernan and Harrison Schmitt concluded the lunar explorations with Apollo 17, this worldly nine-year-old had come to accept men on the Moon as a predictable – if still thrilling – fact. What I remember most from that time are the basics: the constant presence of the television, the brief riveting drama of liftoff, and the interminable waiting and commentary by the pundits and news anchors. The coverage was leavened only infrequently by stilted and grainy inflight video transmissions, and proved overall to be substantially less interesting than the rich fantasy life of the young space adventurer. Neil Armstrong's strange and murky television image setting first foot on the Moon is seared into the world's collective brain, mine included, but more vivid for me are the eerie rhythms of radio communication between the astronauts and ground control in Houston – that inimitable *beeeep*, followed by the most spacious silence imaginable. Those key sounds come back clearly, along with certain visual icons. How can I forget the ghostly Saturn V rocket rising up over Florida on a column of fearful flame, over and over and over again in my parents' living room, as the years passed and they went about their domestic routine? The era ended quickly, just as the world and the boy began to take it for granted, and we all moved on.

Twenty-five years elapsed until I thought much about Apollo again. This time, it was as a photographer with a particular interest in exploration and landscape issues. At a certain point in my own work I had realized that a landscape is a landscape, whether made on Earth, the Moon, or Mars, and had become fascinated with the differences and similarities between images of our home ground and those of other worlds. The Moon held a particular attraction, however. While robotic probes had traveled most of the solar system since 1972 and had radioed their extraordinary images back to Earth throughout, the only celestial realm humans had actually traveled to and photographed in person was the Moon. I was also especially taken with the way the Moon's spare physical characteristics offered a distillation of traditional landscape vocabulary, a kind of pure and elemental dialogue between minerals and radiation, an epiphany of rock and light.

Certainly my interest had shifted from the boyish fascination of years past, but deep down I must admit to being driven by essentially the same forces: I still wanted to be an astronaut. More precisely, I suppose, I wanted to be an extraterrestrial photographer. Needless to say, I faced some formidable obstacles to realizing such an ambition, so I settled for investigating the next-best thing available, the inflight photographs that the Apollo astronauts had already made. The pictures I was familiar with were the twenty or so well-worn images that we all know, the iconic photographs that were selected at the time by the editors of magazines like *Life* and *National Geographic*, and that have come to define a certain part of late-twentieth-century visual culture. No pictures are more famous – Apollo 8's orbital earthrise over the Moon, Buzz Aldrin triumphantly facing Armstrong's lens on Apollo 11, the whole Earth of Apollo 17 floating so delicately alone in the indifferent velvet of the void – and they deserve to be, having completely transformed the way humans conceive of themselves, but they also suffer from over-exposure. I had chanced across a few of the astronauts' more obscure black-and-white images in a small exhibition catalog, however, and their spare beauty and quality of light showed a different Moon than the one we had all collectively come to know, a freshly compelling one. I had a hunch there was more, and in 1994 resolved to visit NASA and discover just how much. What I found in a small, windowless concrete bunker that autumn in Houston, Texas, came to occupy me for the next four years and has resulted in this book.

The Apollo inflight photographic archive is extraordinary. First, it's vast: the astronauts exposed miles of 70mm hand-held Hasselblad black-and-white negatives and color transparencies, as well as monitored giant automatic mapping cameras on the later missions that shot 5" x 5" and panoramic images of the lunar surface from orbit. Altogether more than 17,000 hand-held and 15,000 automatic orbital photographic images were made. Secondly, the archive has depth as well as breadth: the space explorers photographed just about everything, all the time, and the different lunar landscapes that each successive mission visited were varied and hauntingly beautiful. Finally, the overall quality and technical proficiency of the images are stunning. The pictures are so sharp and crisp they verge on the surreal; that they were made in a vacuum certainly helps, but there is no question that the astronauts knew how to operate their cameras superbly.

+ + +

NASA's interest in documenting its missions was not always so strong; Mercury astronaut John Glenn, for example, was forced to buy a cheap 35mm camera at a Cocoa Beach drugstore in 1962 because he alone felt that America's first orbital spaceflight merited some historic snapshots. Over time, however, the agency realized the public-relations value of inflight photography, and by the Gemini program had made a serious commitment to it, giving the astronauts medium-format Hasselblad cameras. Apollo raised the ante; the documentary needs of the scientific-exploration community and lobbying by certain of the more visually inclined astronauts encouraged NASA to provide elaborate equipment, precious time to use it in the tight flight plans, and extensive training to men who were some of the world's greatest test pilots, but certainly not landscape photographers. For the most part, the astronauts took up the additional challenges of photography and lunar surface geology with enthusiasm and skill, shooting ten-to-twenty-image panoramas at each rock-sampling site, as well as multiple views of each rock destined for the sampling bag, shots of the soil itself after the rock was removed, and final shots of the site in relation to larger surrounding features. Beyond their memories, the astronauts were able to bring back only a few precious things from their odyssey: numerical data from experiments, 838 pounds of lunar rock, film and video footage, and the trove of more than 32,000 still pictures. It is the photographic imagery that has proved most useful over the years to the planetary geologists, astrophysicists, and astronomers attempting to reconstruct the history of the Moon from the eighty short hours humans have actually walked its surface.

If there is a single distinguishing characteristic of the Apollo imagery, it would have to be its primary function as a clear and precise documentary measuring tool, a function reinforced by that most essential of NASA visual leitmotifs: the reseau-line lens grid, whose small, repeating plus-signs were literally burned into the film of most images at the moment of exposure. In effect, the reseau lens grid turns every Apollo photograph into a miniature map of the Moon, which is of course exactly what the scientists required and NASA intended. In this way, the Apollo photographs openly admit the biases and goals of their culture like few other documentary survey images made before or since. Apollo was nothing if not a culture of numbers, numbers moved about with unparalleled precision and competence. The program marshalled the full extent of human powers of measuring, organizing, testing, quantifying, navigating, sampling, and exploring, and focused them intensely on a famously elusive and difficult goal. Apollo was a resounding success by any measure, not least the proud fact that despite the tremendous risks, it suffered not a single inflight casualty. Numerical and quantitative precision was crucial.

The world the astronauts found, after the longest and fastest journey yet experienced by humankind, can be described in a litany of extremes. Most crucially, the Moon had been pristine for over four and a half billion years before the arrival of its first lucky life forms in the incarnation of Neil Armstrong and Edwin Aldrin. It is still, silent, and without water erosion; the one breeze that blows there is the solar wind, ceaselessly bearing an endless bombardment of cosmic rays. Time as measured by the cycles of the Sun is radically different on the Moon, with the lunar day and night each equivalent to fourteen days on Earth. The light and heat from the Sun itself are also profoundly stronger. Without an atmosphere, visible light becomes blinding and dangerous solar radiation; temperature swings on the Moon are particularly dramatic, ranging from 273 degrees Fahrenheit in full sunshine in the lunar summer to minus 244 degrees in the shade of lunar winter. The temperature differential between light and shadow, inches apart, that an astronaut might typically encounter ranges from about 135 degrees Fahrenheit in the sunlight to about minus 150 degrees in the shade. Each landing was thus carefully timed to coincide with the lunar "morning," both for its relative coolness and the low, contrasting angle of sunlight that it provided, which greatly aided visibility.

Moving about was particularly difficult because in the hyperclear, atmosphereless lunar environment all the astronauts found it impossible to accurately gauge space, distance, and scale. The human brain has evolved in tandem with human mobility, but exclusively on Earth and always in the presence of atmospheric haze – those purples and blues that build in density the farther the eye looks into the horizon give an idea of distance. Other life forms like trees and brush help engender a sense of scale, as does the presence of man-made objects of a known size, but the Moon of course lacks these elements entirely. Additionally, the Moon's geological features tend to look soft and diminutive, due to the nature of meteoric erosion and the thick layer of attendant dust, but nothing could be more deceptive. The small inviting hills depicted in the photographic panoramas of Apollo 15, for example, are really mountains that tower 15,000 feet above their valley floor. Adding to the confusion, accurate color perception was almost impossible on the Moon's surface: though any two astronauts rarely agreed on the exact color of a particular lunar feature, all concurred that the color of the highly reflective lunar soil changed with the angle and direction of sunlight, ranging all the way from a "mouse-brown" tan with backlit illumination to a "concrete gray" when lit from the side. For viewers on Earth, the photographic process itself also added its own alterations to the "true" color of the Moon: the color film emulsions used were formulated to capture the spectrum of light in an Earth atmosphere; without one, they carry "inaccurate" tonal casts of blues and greens.

Above all else in this disorienting and dangerous environment, the astronauts had to be canny and relentless geologists each moment they walked on the lunar surface. They relayed a constant scientific voice description of what they were seeing to Houston, decided which rocks among the millions before them were special enough to take up limited cargo space on the journey home, and – last but not least – they photographically documented almost every step on the lunar surface with dogged thoroughness for later scientific examination on Earth. On the Moon, each man carried a chest-mounted Hasselblad medium-format camera fitted with a standard 80mm lens, oversized controls to compensate for bulky spacesuit gloves, and a special Kodak film pack that carried 160 exposures for color transparency material and 200 for black-and-white. Focus and exposure were set manually; film advance was motorized. Additional camera bodies were available, along with a selection of 105mm, 250mm, and 500mm lenses for special situations, but the vast majority of lunar surface images were shot from the chest alone, without the compositional benefit of an eye looking through a viewfinder. Though they trained extensively on Earth to master framing control of the chest-mounted cameras, particularly during the panoramic sequences, it is safe to say that the astronauts were not artists, nor would they want to be seen as such. In general, they sought a transparently accurate filmic trace of their surroundings, not a personal interpretation of them.

Yet for all the duress and haste under which they worked, the astronaut photographers were certainly not robots. Their images, while neutral and often taking on the cold, measured characteristics of the reseau grid, do not carry a truly robotic stare; theirs were very human eyes that repeatedly blinked and widened in response to the majesty and surreality of their temporary surroundings. The range of what they thought was important enough to document is particularly impressive, and those rare moments when they allowed their private thoughts to intrude on the photographic record – like Charles Duke's haunting image of a picture of his family carefully laid on the lunar soil – are moving reminders that despite the lack of time for reflection and their famous reticence, the astronauts were painfully aware of the multiple meanings of their presence on the Moon. Occasionally, they produced a masterpiece, though it is doubtful that they knew it at the moment of exposure.

I will never forget my astonishment the first time I was able to examine the "master dupe" film roll of Apollo 11, re-enacting the exact steps and photographic decision-making of Armstrong and Aldrin frame by frame as they walked for the first time on the surface of another celestial body. This was as close as I'd ever get to the Moon; not quite seeing with the eyes of one actually there, but at least able to look through the lens of their camera. As I studied the images of each successively more ambitious mission, picture by picture, I realized that though I'd never get to make my own imagery on the Moon as an artist, there was plenty of room to make my own particular version of it from the archive itself. *Full Moon* imagines and then constructs the story of a single mission from what I feel to be some of the most memorable photography of the actual multiple missions. It also consciously sets out to frame the images in a different context from that in which they were made and most often have been seen, stripping them of immediate textual scientific descriptions, chronological order, and any references to Earth-bound views.

I began the editing process very simply, by quickly picking those images that were most beautiful and interesting to me, decisions that were of course subject to the strengths and weaknesses of my own visual taste. An informed viewer, for example, can see some of the undercurrents that have shaped my aesthetic by the many references in the book to both contemporary landscape photographers and those of the past, especially those who worked on the government-funded American "railroad surveys" of the 1870s. In general, I tried to keep away from the more famous of the Apollo images, but finally realized that certain ones had become so for good reason, and had to be in the book. Where would we be as a visual culture without Aldrin's Apollo 11 footprint, or Apollo 17's whole Earth? They are astounding photographs. I was pleased to discover, however, that the previously unpublished black-and-white Apollo 8 earthrise I had selected for the book was actually the first such image made; the coarser and now famous color earthrise shots came after a hurried switch of cameras.

Beyond concerns of personal taste and historic necessity, I sought all the fresh material I could find, attempting to collect images that offered the viewer a sense of direct experience, of actually being there: the hasty blurred glance, the pile of trash at the base of the lunar module, a glimpse of the Moon passing by below through an orbital porthole, a lunar landscape so empty it seems almost transparent. Along with immediacy, however, I also wanted to emphasize a sense of intimacy: the fragile humanness of the Apollo endeavor drove me to try and find every decent inflight portrait the astronauts made of each other. There aren't many; most of the faces in the book come from Apollo 7, the program's maiden voyage which, like Apollo 9, never left Earth orbit and whose astronauts had slightly more time on their hands than the others. Lunar surface portraits are even rarer, and I chose a single image of Eugene Cernan, commander of Apollo 17, to represent all the twelve men who walked on the lunar surface. Unlike the other faces in the book, which tend towards a certain steely-eyed, stubbly romanticism, Cernan's image is anti-heroic and profoundly vulnerable. Just out of his suit and back in the lunar module from the last moonwalk of the Apollo program, he leans back exhausted in his underwear, filthy with lunar soil, and looks equally as if he might smile in perfect satisfaction at a job well done, or break out in tears.

Some might wonder why I included images from the Earth-orbital Gemini program in a book about Apollo and the Moon; I did so because the power of Jim McDivitt's 1965 images of Edward White's Gemini IV spacewalk has never been equalled by any of the subsequent Apollo spacewalk photographs, nor by anything since. McDivitt's images alone manage to convey both the whirling, vertiginous disorientation of a zero-gravity stroll and its sense of playful delight; they perform a crucial role in the book as an antidote to so many of the pictures that are about a controlled, gridded, and measured mastery. Indeed, they balance the overall thrust of Apollo: for once, we see the loss of navigational coordinates rather than the result of their triumph. The spacewalk photographs depict the disappearance of a particular spatial orientation and a gleeful abandonment of directionality. Perhaps even more important, though, they establish the book's sense of scale early on: the gulf between the intimately human on the one hand and the incomprehensible void on the other.

This dialectic of scale is one of the most salient aspects of any landscape photography, and is greatly magnified as one ventures beyond the cocoon of the Earth's atmosphere. The old vocabulary of the sublime gains new words in outer space, and certainly the mythic aspects of Apollo – the small, vulnerable human venturing out into the heart of the unknown (and perhaps even the unknowable) – were one of the things that drew me to the archive in the first place. Speaking of the open sweeps of the American West, the photographer Robert Adams writes: "Among reasons for enjoying space is the proof it offers of our small size." Following that line of thought, I selected all the images from the archive that I thought eloquently described scale, including those that removed any sense of it at all. Interestingly, however, the more classic rules of the sublime that Adams expresses do not apply as definitively in outer space as they do among the open places on Earth; the situation is more complex here. The comprehensive aerial vantage point offered by journeys like Apollo, for example, is both humbling and aggrandizing to the viewer. The astronaut indeed has only the thin spacecraft wall separating him from the cold cosmos beyond, but he also enjoys a truly God-like view and empyrean perspective unknown to any previous age. The space traveler is both gigantically empowered, and reminded at every turn of his utter inconsequence.

Issues of big and small comprise but one half of the sublime landscape; for me, the other is the rule of light itself. Concerns about light always lurked behind all the others that drove my selection, and so to me the archive's most important images will always remain the black-and-white ones, in part because their finer grain carries a higher visual acuity and renders more detail, but mostly because of the way they distill light in a world without air. In a poem about stars, Charles Simic writes of being "consumed by and converted into light," and it's an accurate summary of how many of the black-and-white images make me feel, whether they might describe a spectacular and pristine lunar surface from orbit, or the banal base of the rickety lunar module scattered with detritus. Subject matter becomes less important than illumination itself: here, the best of the black-and-white images share a kind of delineation through distilled light that is at once highly abstract and yet brutally representational, a combination I have yet to see anywhere else and one that makes me feel like I enjoy divine powers of perception. Truthfully, humans were physically never meant to see so clearly and penetratingly, without an atmosphere to soften the edges of the physical world and protect them from the more overwhelming aspects of the Sun's illuminating force. For me, these images are charged tracings of a world perceptually and biologically beyond the pale, amazingly revealed not to some robotic probe but to fellow mortals. To view them, even from the safety of Earth, is to feel both ecstatic and imperiled.

+ + +

The story that *Full Moon* tells in its three parts is perhaps a familiar one to those nations that have historically pursued policies of terrestrial expansion, as well as to those cultures that suffered their intrusion. For America, Apollo was a chance to take its old driving myths of Manifest Destiny and an endless frontier, and symbolically reignite them on a scale as vast as the cosmos. This time, however, there was slightly less of a dark side: for once in the history of human exploration into "unknown" spaces, there was no one else already there – the Moon was indeed truly "virgin" before we set foot on it, and has remained conflict-free thereafter. I have tried to make the first section of the book follow fairly closely the outlines of this classic tale of Eden attained: the Moon appears from above as an abstract symphony of pristine splendor.

The second section on the lunar surface, however, shows a more complex reality, one that idealizing myths of expansion and exploration are generally reluctant to dwell upon: the fact that the instant humans arrive (whether indigenous peoples or those who follow) they begin to alter their environment, and not always for the better. In this case, the astronauts' reasons for being on the Moon were to poke, prod, measure, and steal it for hungry consumption back on Earth, and they used every tool they had available for the purpose, as humans generally will. I have not shied away in the book from depicting this primally egocentric human activity, finding it as moving and important as the timeless grace of the Moon itself, which I also have tried to emphasize. This is not an apologia for our behavior, but rather the only truthful way to recount what happened. Tools and footprints and tracks, matched with a self-absorption unparalleled in the animal kingdom, are much of what humans are made of. Exploration of places we've not been to before etches the story sharper than normal, and sometimes the tale is one of sad destruction as much as thrilling enlightenment and shattering reevaluations of our place in the Universe.

Perhaps what is most interesting about the Apollo saga, however, is that finally it marks a major break from the typical dynamics of historical exploration and territorial expansionism. It is a leave-taking of such unprecedented grandeur and scale that it paradoxically doubles back on itself. Rather than embodying a linear progression to a new world that discards the old in pursuit of endless freedom and limitless bounty, Apollo's path is circular. Humanity's boldest and most audacious movement outward from its home found itself relentlessly looking in the opposite direction – back toward Earth – from the moment it began. The missions proved that if an explorer pushes far enough past the edge of the distant, promising, and linear horizon it will disappear entirely, reemerging transformed as a naked and open circle. In the same way that the capability of the atomic bomb has rendered conflict on the largest scale moot, the Apollo missions have annihilated the last shreds of expansionist mythology: the concept that Earth can continue to offer people and nations infinite resources, that progress implies a liberation from responsibility, or that we can truthfully call anywhere else home.

Michael Light

Jacket: Leaving the scene of their explorations, the Apollo 15 astronauts photograph the Moon's southern hemisphere shortly after firing their rocket engine to begin the trip back to Earth. The image includes a portion of the lunar farside, which is not visible from Earth. This view was captured by a high-resolution camera stored in the side of the service module. Metric mapping camera black-and-white negative by Alfred Worden, Apollo 15, July 26–August 7, 1971.

Boards: The battered highlands of the lunar farside, seen from some 750 miles at the start of Apollo 16's return to Earth. Visible on the front cover are craters Saha at center top and Moiseëv at center bottom, while 47-mile-wide Crater King with its distinctive "lobster claw" interior appears to the far left on the rear cover, with a portion of Crater Lobachevsky at the lower right. Each cover shows an approximately 200-mile-wide square section. Metric mapping camera black-and-white negative by Kenneth Mattingly, Apollo 16, April 16–27, 1972.

Preliminary Spread I: Billowing exhaust smoke, the 5 massive first-stage engines of the Apollo 11 Saturn rocket ignite to begin the 238,000-mile journey that would land Neil Armstrong and Buzz Aldrin on the surface of the Moon days later. One of the rocket's 4 fins, labeled with the letter "B" for clear identification, appears through the exhaust gases. NASA ran between 20 and 30 remote-controlled and fire-insulated motion-picture cameras close to the engines during each Apollo launch, to have a record for later analysis in case of any malfunction. Fortunately, this safety footage never had to be used for its intended purpose on any of the Apollo missions. Remote-controlled motion-picture camera film still, Apollo 11, July 16, 1969.

Preliminary Spread II: Mounted directly underneath the Saturn rocket, a camera captures the exact instant of ignition of one of the rocket's 5 F-1 engines. Remote-controlled motion-picture camera film still, Apollo 11, July 16, 1969.

Preliminary Spread III: An instant later, the camera captures the growing yellow fireball of kerosene and pure oxygen that will soon turn into a white-hot wall of flame exceeded in power only by a nuclear explosion. Cameras, equipment, and the launch pad itself were doused with a constant spray of water during Apollo launches, to prevent damage from the searing heat and blast of the rocket's exhaust and also to suppress the deafening roar. Remote-controlled motion-picture camera film still, Apollo 11, July 16, 1969.

1. The first test flight of the Apollo Saturn V Moon rocket. At liftoff the 363-foot vehicle weighed 6,220,025 pounds, with the first-stage engines producing 7,500,000 pounds of thrust and burning 15 tons of fuel per second. Color transparency taken by the Intermediate Ground Optical Recording Camera (IGOR) shortly after liftoff, Apollo 4 (unmanned), November 9, 1967.

2. About 41 miles above Earth the first stage of the Saturn V rocket is depleted; it separates with a plume of smoke and flame. An instant later, the 5 engines of the second stage will ignite and burn for another 6.5 minutes, boosting the rocket to an altitude of 116 miles. Color transparency made by a 70mm tracking camera on a U.S. Air Force chase plane flying at 40,000 feet, Apollo 11, July 16, 1969.

3. Stage separation of an unmanned Saturn IB rocket. The IB was a smaller test version of the Saturn V, lacking its massive first stage entirely and producing only 1.6 million pounds of thrust. In a Saturn V flight, the stage pictured here dropping away would be the second and would have occurred at 116 miles altitude; ignition of the third stage would take place an instant later. Color transparency made from a high-altitude U.S. Air Force chase plane, Apollo 5 (unmanned), January 22, 1968.

4. Film still taken by an onboard automatic motion-picture camera mounted on the second stage of the Saturn V rocket, about 41 miles above Earth, just as the first stage falls away after 148 seconds of burn time. In this second test flight of the Saturn V, exposed film was ejected in a special parachute-equipped protective capsule for reentry into Earth's atmosphere and recovery in the Atlantic off Cape Kennedy, Florida. Apollo 6 (unmanned), April 4, 1968.

5. The cabin of the Apollo command module, showing the side hatchway with a sliver of Earth showing through its window above the three crew couches. At 212 cubic feet, it offered each astronaut about as much room as a phone booth. Apollo 9, the second of the manned Earth testing missions, was in orbit for 10 days and tested the entire Apollo spacecraft, particularly the lunar module landing vehicle. Hasselblad 70mm transparency probably by David Scott, Apollo 9, March 3–13, 1969.

6. The spent third stage of the Saturn V launch vehicle floats in Earth orbital vacuum, crystals of ice lining the surface of its liquid hydrogen tank. Hasselblad 70mm transparency probably by David Scott, Apollo 9, March 3–13, 1969.

7. Walter Schirra, commander of the first manned Apollo flight, gazes out the hatch window into the glare of sunlight in a vacuum. The 10-day Earth-orbital shakedown of men and equipment went flawlessly, but the stakes for Apollo 7 – the first to be manned after the tragic launch-pad fire that killed the crew of Apollo 1 and very nearly the entire Apollo program – were tremendous. Hasselblad 70mm transparency by Walter Cunningham, Apollo 7, October 11–22, 1968.

8. The Florida peninsula looking east into the Sun, seen from an altitude of about 138 miles. Hasselblad 70mm transparency by Walter Cunningham, Apollo 7, October 11–22, 1968.

9. Astronaut David Scott floats in the hatchway of the command module Gumdrop during a spacewalk about 140 miles above the Earth. Scott was photographed by crewmate Russell Schweickart, who was making his own spacewalk to test the new space suit and backpack designed for moonwalking astronauts. Hasselblad 70mm transparency, Apollo 9, March 3–13, 1969.

10. Edward White tumbles weightlessly over the Gulf of Mexico in the first, enduringly spectacular American spacewalk, on June 3, 1965. Spacewalking was a key goal of the Earth-orbit flights of NASA's Gemini program, which was created to demonstrate techniques crucial for Apollo. In the 23 minutes White spent outside the cabin, he and his spacecraft sped from California to the South Atlantic at 17,500 mph. Hasselblad 70mm transparency by James McDivitt, Gemini 4, June 3–7, 1965.

11. Sun reflecting off the Pacific Ocean, covered with a layer of stratocumulus clouds some 4,000 feet above the water. Hasselblad 70mm transparency made from about 160 miles, probably by Ronald Evans, Apollo 17, December 7–19, 1972.

12. Edward White spacewalking above the Texas coastline. His suit had 21 layers of thermal and micrometeoroid protection, a double gold-plated visor to cut the unfiltered solar rays, and an oxygen chestpack with an 8-minute emergency reserve. Hasselblad 70mm transparency by James McDivitt, Gemini 4, June 3–7, 1965.

13. Edward White over the Gulf of Mexico, showing the open door of the Gemini spacecraft and his crewmate photographing in the hatch. The two astronauts' elation at the first spacewalk was palpable, with McDivitt exclaiming, "You look beautiful, Ed," and White replying, "I feel like a million dollars!" Hasselblad 70mm transparency by James McDivitt, Gemini 4, June 3–7, 1965.

14. Sunset reflected in the ocean with some lens flare, photographed from an altitude of about 120 miles above the Earth. Hasselblad 70mm transparency by Walter Schirra, Apollo 7, October 11–22, 1968.

15. The very first glimmers of dawn, showing the horizon transformed into a series of vivid bands of color due to sunlight refracted by the atmosphere. Hasselblad 70mm transparency probably by James McDivitt, Gemini 4, June 3–7, 1965.

16. Hurricane Gladys over the Gulf of Mexico, 150 miles southwest of Tampa, Florida, from an orbital altitude of 112 miles. Wind speeds in the hurricane were 80 mph. Hasselblad 70mm transparency by Walter Cunningham, Apollo 7, October 11–22, 1968.

17. Commander Walter Schirra with a head cold, particularly troublesome in zero gravity because sinuses cannot drain normally. Hasselblad 70mm transparency by Walter Cunningham, Apollo 7, October 11–22, 1968.

18. Inside a Moon-bound command module, the astronauts' flight plan is held against the instrument panel by a bungee cord, ready for consultation. Hasselblad 70mm transparency by Stuart Roosa, Apollo 14, January 31–February 9, 1971.

19. Earth terminator, looking south along the coast of East Africa several hours prior to splashdown; Hasselblad 70mm transparency by Michael Collins, Apollo 11, July 16–24, 1969.

20. Commander James Lovell sleeping as best he could in lunar module temperatures in the low 40s during the crippled flight of Apollo 13. At 200,000 miles from the Earth, an oxygen tank explosion rendered the command module Odyssey useless. Apollo 13 was regarded as a "successful failure" by NASA, because all three astronauts were returned to Earth alive against tremendous odds. Hasselblad 70mm transparency probably by Jack Swigert, Apollo 13, April 11–17, 1970.

21. A slim crescent Earth seen on the journey homeward from the Moon, showing golden clouds and a bright oceanic reflection at the terminator, or edge of night. Hasselblad 70mm transparency probably by Richard Gordon, Apollo 12, November 14–24, 1969.

22. Approaching their destination, the astronauts saw the Moon as a slender crescent. The bluish coloration is an effect produced inside the camera by lens flare. Hasselblad 70mm transparency probably by Stuart Roosa, Apollo 14, January 31–February 9, 1971.

23. A half-Moon seen from the command module on the way back to Earth, showing several examples of the vast dark volcanic plains known in Latin as "mare," or "seas." Moving counterclockwise are the Sea of Serenity, the Sea of Tranquillity, and the Sea of Fertility, with the Sea of Crises above. Hasselblad 70mm black-and-white negative probably by Alfred Worden, Apollo 15, July 26–August 7, 1971.

24. The southern hemisphere of the Moon as seen on the return to Earth. Craters Pasteur, Hilbert, Scaliger, Milne, and Schroedinger's Rille lie along the terminator, or line that separates lunar night from day, with Humboldt Crater to the center of the image and Smyth's Sea to the right. Metric mapping camera black-and-white negative by Alfred Worden, Apollo 15, July 26–August 7, 1971.

25. The Ocean of Storms can be seen at the top of this lunar orbital image, with the Known Sea at the bottom. The rugged highland region of the Riphaeus Mountains bisects the two, having been high enough to have survived the lava flooding that created this vast volcanic plain. North to the top right, 7-mile-wide crater Euclides to the top left. Metric mapping camera black-and-white negative by Kenneth Mattingly, Apollo 16, April 16–27, 1972.

26. Visible are craters Arzachel at the left, Alphonsus to the center, and Ptolemaeus to the right in this orbital view made at an altitude of 68 miles. Alphonsus is 67 miles wide. Metric mapping camera black-and-white negative made by Kenneth Mattingly, Apollo 16, April 16–27, 1972.

27. A forbidding landscape created by debris that was ejected during the formation of the giant Imbrium impact basin. This so-called Imbrium sculpture affects large portions of the lunar nearside. Ridges and grooves point toward the center of the Imbrium basin, which is several hundred miles away. Metric mapping camera black-and-white negative at an altitude of 68 miles, by Kenneth Mattingly, Apollo 16, April 16–27, 1972.

28. Crater Krieger, 12 miles in diameter, seen through one of the windows of the command module Endeavor from an orbital altitude of 66 miles (see caption 128). Hasselblad 70mm black-and-white negative by Alfred Worden, Apollo 15, July 26–August 7, 1971.

29. An enlarged detail of the battered highlands of the lunar farside, seen from some 1,000 miles at the start of Apollo 16's return to Earth. The 47-mile-wide Crater King, with its distinctive center in the shape of a lobster claw, can be seen to the left. Metric mapping camera black-and-white negative by Kenneth Mattingly, Apollo 16, April 16–27, 1972.

30. Earthrise seen for the first time by human eyes. Apollo 8 astronaut William Anders took this photograph, which looks southwest toward Crater Gibbs from an orbital altitude of about 70 miles. For years after the mission, commander Frank Borman claimed to have made the picture, but onboard voice recordings reveal that this photo, as well as the more famous color views taken immediately after, were made by Anders. Hasselblad 70mm black-and-white negative, Apollo 8, December 24, 1968.

31. Battered highlands on the lunar farside, looking south in a view covering an area about the size of Switzerland. Hasselblad 70mm black-and-white negative probably by Michael Collins, Apollo 11, July 16–24, 1969.

32. An enlarged detail of the crater Godin, about 27 miles wide, seen from an altitude of 69 miles and located in the highland region that separates the Sea of Tranquillity from the Central Bay. Hasselblad 70mm black-and-white negative probably by John Young, Apollo 10, May 18–26, 1969.

33. Crater Messier in the Sea of Fertility, seen from an altitude of 70 miles with a 500mm telephoto lens. Messier is believed to have been formed by a low-angle meteoric impact, creating a furrow 5 miles wide and 9 miles long. Hasselblad 70mm black-and-white negative probably by Alfred Worden, Apollo 15, July 26–August 7, 1971.

34. Photographic composite of Hadley Rille from an orbital altitude of 70 miles, showing the Apollo 15 landing site in the lower right of the upper photograph, just below the rille. The Apennine mountains are visible to the right in the upper photograph, and show about 15,000 feet of relief; Hadley Rille itself is almost a mile wide and 1,000 feet deep near the landing site (see captions 72 and 73). Hasselblad 70mm black-and-white negatives, by Alfred Worden, Apollo 15, July 26–August 7, 1971.

35. Crater Deseilligny, photographed from an orbit 75 miles above the lunar surface in the Sea of Serenity. The low ridges, called wrinkle ridges, were formed as the vast lava plain cooled. Deseilligny is 4 miles wide. Metric mapping camera black-and-white negative by Ronald Evans, Apollo 17, December 7–19, 1972.

36. 10-mile-wide Crater Bessel, with Crater Deseilligny above, photographed 69 miles above the lunar surface in the Sea of Serenity. The area shown is about 105 square miles. Metric mapping camera black-and-white negative by Ronald Evans, Apollo 17, December 7–19, 1972.

37. The metric mapping camera, operating automatically, took this sequence of pictures as the command module Endeavor drifted over the nearside crater Timocharis 62 miles below. This view is one of hundreds obtained by command module pilot Alfred Worden while his crewmates explored the lunar surface. Timocharis is 20 miles wide. Metric mapping camera black-and-white negatives, Apollo 15, July 26–August 7, 1971.

38. Timocharis Crater, Apollo 15.

39. Timocharis Crater, Apollo 15.

40. Timocharis Crater, Apollo 15.

41. Floodlit by the morning Sun, the lunar highlands to the west of the Sea of Tranquillity stand out in stark relief. The twin craters Sabine and Ritter can be seen to the upper left, with 7-mile-wide crater Schmidt to the center of the image. Hasselblad 70mm black-and-white negative made from an altitude of about 70 miles, probably by Michael Collins, Apollo 11, July 16–24, 1969.

42. The command module America photographed from the ascent stage of the lunar module Challenger just before docking and the return of the moonwalking astronauts to their orbiting colleague. The Sea of Fertility is visible below, as the dark surface area on the upper right horizon. Hasselblad 70mm transparency by Harrison Schmitt, Apollo 17, December 7–19, 1972.

43. Readying for final descent, the lunar module Intrepid floats 69 miles above the giant crater Ptolemaeus in this westward-looking view, after having separated from the command module Yankee Clipper. The circular crater in the middle distance on the right is Herschel. Touchdown for Intrepid will be on the Ocean of Storms. Hasselblad 70mm transparency by Richard Gordon, Apollo 12, November 14–24, 1969.

44. A view of lunar module *Intrepid*'s shadow from the commander's window, just after landing and prior to surface excursions on the Ocean of Storms. The lander is 23 feet tall. Hasselblad 70mm black-and-white negative by Alan Bean, Apollo 12, November 14–24, 1969.

45. Astronaut's shadow. Hasselblad 70mm black-and-white negative by Harrison Schmitt, Apollo 17, December 7–19, 1972.

46. Unfiltered by any atmosphere, the Sun as seen from the lunar surface is more brilliant than on Earth. Lens flare creates the bluish cast seen in this photograph. The Apollo landings took place during the early lunar morning, with the Sun about 12 degrees above the horizon, to aid the astronauts to spot craters and boulders. Hasselblad 70mm transparency near Surveyor Crater by Charles Conrad, Apollo 12, November 14–24, 1969.

47. Apollo 11 moonwalker Edwin "Buzz" Aldrin took this unusual close-up photograph of pristine lunar soil by hand-holding the camera above the ground. Moments later, he would disturb this aeons-old patch of ground with his own boot. Hasselblad 70mm transparency, Apollo 11, July 16–24, 1969.

48. Aldrin's boot print, in an image that has come to symbolize human exploration of the Moon. The fine dust clearly records the pattern of treads on the sole of the boot. Scientists estimate that the constant rain of micrometeorites onto the Moon is sufficient to churn the uppermost half-inch of lunar soil every 10 million years. Accordingly, this footprint should last one or two million years. Hasselblad 70mm transparency by Edwin Aldrin, Apollo 11, July 16–24, 1969.

49. Alan Bean at Sharp Crater with the handtool carrier near his right hand. On the carrier are visible the cuplike sample bags and the large sample collection bag that fills its center. Hasselblad 70mm black-and-white negative by Charles Conrad, Apollo 12, November 14–24, 1969.

50. Edwin Aldrin carrying a package of scientific experiments to a deployment site south of the lunar module *Eagle*. In his left hand is a seismometer (see caption 57) used to test hypotheses about the inner composition of the Moon, and in his right, a laser-ranging retro-reflector experiment used to measure its exact distance from the Earth. Hasselblad 70mm transparency by Neil Armstrong, Apollo 11, July 16–24, 1969.

51. The lunar module *Antares* at Fra Mauro, with the intense Sun just behind. Astronauts Alan Shepard and Edgar Mitchell fondly referred to their lunar home and oasis as "jewel-like." Hasselblad 70mm transparency by Alan Shepard, Apollo 14, January 31–February 9, 1971.

52. The descent engine bell and leg of lunar module *Intrepid*, showing the cylindrical tube of the nuclear fuel cask to the upper right; its fuel element has just been placed in the radioisotope thermoelectric generator (RTG) (see caption 56), a small nuclear power station that will power several lunar surface experiments for years to come. Hasselblad 70mm black-and-white negative by Alan Bean, Apollo 12, November 14–24, 1969.

53. Using an experiment nicknamed "the thumper," Edgar Mitchell detonates a small explosive charge to create a miniature "moonquake." Wires leading from the thumper carry sensors to measure the vibrations produced, which reveal information about the structure of the lunar surface. In the background is a crater the astronauts have christened "Old Nameless." Hasselblad 70mm transparency by Alan Shepard, Apollo 14, January 31–February 9, 1971.

54. Because the Moon has no atmosphere, it is an ideal place to study the solar wind, the stream of subatomic particles emitted by the Sun. Pictured is the solar wind composition experiment (SWC), a strip of foil measuring 4.5 feet by 1 foot. Each square centimeter was peppered with 6 to 7 million solar wind particles each second, and was left out for 18 hours before being packed up for return to scientists on Earth. Hasselblad 70mm black-and-white negative by Alan Bean, Apollo 12, November 14–24, 1969.

55. Alan Bean deploying experiments on the lunar surface; the blue aura that surrounds him is thought to be water-vapor ice crystals emitted from the boiler on his space-suit backpack, though neither Bean nor his commander reported seeing such vapor from the backpacks on the surface. Hasselblad 70mm transparency by Charles Conrad, Apollo 12, November 14–24, 1969.

56. On 5 of the 6 missions, the astronauts deployed the Apollo lunar surface experiments package (ALSEP). The ALSEP's central station, which transmits data to Earth, is at rear, outfitted with gold Mylar insulation. In front sits the radioisotope thermoelectric generator (RTG). Inside, a plutonium-238 fuel capsule (see caption 52) generates a temperature of 1,350 degrees F. Thermocouples convert this energy into power for the experiments. Hasselblad 70mm transparency by Alan Shepard, Apollo 14, January 31–February 9, 1971.

57. ALSEP's lunar seismometer, officially designated the passive seismic experiment (PSE), deployed at the Hadley Plains. The seismometer is surrounded by an apron of aluminized Mylar to reduce fluctuations in surface temperature. Recording moonquakes and meteorite impacts, the seismometer enabled scientists to draw profiles of the lunar interior. Hasselblad 70mm photograph by David Scott, Apollo 15, July 26–August 7, 1971.

58. A snapshot of Charles Duke and his family in their Houston, Texas, backyard, left at the Moon's Descartes Highlands. Hasselblad 70mm transparency by Charles Duke, Apollo 16, April 16–27, 1972.

59. Footprints on the interior slope of Surveyor Crater. In the climax of the Apollo 12 mission, astronauts Charles Conrad and Alan Bean descended into the 656-foot wide crater to visit the unmanned Surveyor III probe, which had landed on the Moon 2½ years earlier. In history's first pinpoint lunar landing, the astronauts touched down only 600 feet from the probe. Hasselblad 70mm black-and-white negative by Alan Bean, Apollo 12, November 14–24, 1969.

60. Having abandoned their hunt for the rim of Cone Crater, astronauts Alan Shepard and Edgar Mitchell visited this boulder field, which shows a 3-foot-high boulder at left. The astronauts did not realize that at this moment they were looking past the rim itself, which was less than 100 feet away. Hasselblad 70mm black-and-white negative by Edgar Mitchell, Apollo 14, January 31–February 9, 1971.

61. A shadow portrait of the Apollo 12 astronauts as they prepared to collect rock and soil samples. At right sits a device called a gnomon, to provide a photographic scale by which to judge sizes of features. The gnomon indicated local slope and, by its shadow, the Sun angle; it also included a color bar to help analysts match photographic colors and tones to those of the actual scene. Hasselblad 70mm black-and-white negative by Alan Bean, Apollo 12, November 14–24, 1969.

62. A view of a color and contrast photographic chart which the astronaut has positioned on the sunlit, western wall of a small crater to use as a control photograph. Hasselblad 70mm black-and-white negative by Alan Bean, Apollo 12, November 14–24, 1969.

63. "Contact Rock" at the rim of Cone Crater. In the distance sits the lunar module *Antares*, a tiny speck in the Fra Mauro Highlands. (To find the craft, look at the uppermost row of reseau calibration marks. *Antares* sits to the upper left of the second mark from the photo's right-hand edge.) Hasselblad 70mm black-and-white negative, by Edgar Mitchell, Apollo 14, January 31– February 9, 1971.

64. Commander John Young and the battery-powered lunar rover in a photographic composite of the Descartes Highlands, showing the lunar module *Orion* to the left and Stone Mountain, some 1,600 feet high, to the right. The rover, present on the last three Apollo missions, was able to carry two suited astronauts, their gear and cameras, and several hundred pounds of bagged lunar samples, for miles across the lunar surface. Hasselblad 70mm transparencies by Charles Duke, Apollo 16, April 16–27, 1972.

65. Tracks from the modular equipment transporter (MET) gleam in the harsh lunar sunlight. This view looks east toward the lunar module *Antares*, roughly 600 feet away. Loaded with tools, rock samples, and cameras, the MET would have weighed 150 pounds on Earth but weighed only 25 in the Moon's one-sixth gravity. As a result, its tracks are only ¾ of an inch deep. Hasselblad 70mm transparency by Alan Shepard, Apollo 14, January 31–February 9, 1971.

66. A glance backward on the way to the top of Cone Crater during the second moonwalk of Apollo 14; the edge of the MET is visible at left, its tracks curving out of the frame. Hasselblad 70mm black-and-white negative by Alan Shepard, Apollo 14, January 31–February 9, 1971.

67. Charles Duke seen twice in a photographic composite of Apollo 16's first moonwalk, next to 120-foot-wide Plum Crater in the Descartes Highlands. Stone Mountain, 1,600 feet high and 3 miles distant, forms the skyline to the right. On the left, Duke bores into the lunar soil to extract a core sample; on the right, he moves on to the next task. Hasselblad 70mm transparencies by John Young, Apollo 16, April 16–27, 1972.

68. The southern face of "Saddle Rock"; part of a set of large outcroppings just 75 feet shy of the rim of Cone Crater. This image shows the astronauts' geologic hammer and cuplike sample collection container. Scientists believe these rocks were blasted out of the Moon's crust by the gigantic impact that formed the Imbrium Basin. Hasselblad 70mm black-and-white negative by Edgar Mitchell, Apollo 14, January 31–February 9, 1971.

69. Astronaut Alan Bean holds a special sample container designed to aid studies of the lunar environment. He and Charles Conrad have just filled the container with lunar soil at Sharp Crater on the Ocean of Storms. Bean's checklist for the moonwalk is visible on his left wrist, along with his Hasselblad camera mounted on the control unit on his chest. His gold-plated sun visor clearly reflects Conrad, the photographer. Hasselblad 70mm black-and-white negative, Apollo 12, November 14–24, 1969.

70. Commander David Scott test-drives the first manned lunar rover on Apollo 15's first surface excursion; note the orbital lunar photographs used as an aid to navigation. The rover weighed 462 pounds on Earth but only 77 on the Moon, and accordingly gave quite a spirited ride. Seat-belts were mandatory. Hasselblad 70mm black-and-white negative by James Irwin, Apollo 15, July 26–August 7, 1971.

71. Photographic composite of rover tracks looking west on a steep 17-degree grade of Hadley Delta near Spur Crater. At left is the slope that rises to the peak of the mountain, more than 11,000 feet above the Marsh of Decay below. Though the rover was highly mobile, the soft soil and precipitous grade here caused it to begin sliding down the hill when parked. In general, crossing a slope was nerve-racking for the astronaut on the downhill side, but there were no rollovers in any of the missions equipped with a rover. Hasselblad 70mm black-and-white negatives by James Irwin, Apollo 15, July 26–August 7, 1971.

72. Hadley Rille, seen looking northwest from the slopes of Hadley Delta mountain near St. George Crater. Measuring 1 mile across and 1,000 feet deep, the winding canyon is littered with boulders and continues for almost 80 miles along the edge of the Marsh of Decay. Rilles like Hadley may have been formed originally as underground lava tubes, only to have their roofs later bombarded away by aeons of meteoric impact. Hasselblad 70mm black-and-white negative by James Irwin, Apollo 15, July 26–August 7, 1971.

73. The bottom of Hadley Rille, seen looking north from St. George Crater. The clarity of the lunar vacuum and the foreshortening of the telephoto lens offer a deceptively small sense of scale; actually, the largest boulder at the bottom is 45 feet wide. A feature called the Terrace, located on the rille's eastern wall, is visible in the background. Hasselblad 70mm black-and-white negative made with a 500mm lens by David Scott, Apollo 15, July 26–August 7, 1971.

74. A crater, fault scarp, and 7,000-foot mountain are visible in, respectively, the fore, middle, and backgrounds of this image taken at geology station 3 on the way to Shorty Crater from Ballet Crater. This part of the Taurus-Littrow valley was buried when projectiles from the Tycho impact, 1,400 miles to the southwest, started an avalanche. Hasselblad 70mm black-and-white negative by Harrison Schmitt, Apollo 17, December 7–19, 1972.

75. A view of one of the most valuable tools used by the moonwalkers: a set of long-handled tongs, used to pick up rock samples. The tongs were opened and closed by means of a T-shaped handle at the upper end. Space suits worn by the astronauts on the first three lunar landings were very stiff at the waist. Even on the last three landings, which featured more flexible suits, the tongs were essential. Hasselblad 70mm black-and-white negative made near Scarp Crater by David Scott, Apollo 15, July 26–August 7, 1971.

76. At Spur Crater, on the slopes of Hadley Delta, Dave Scott and Jim Irwin discovered a sample of the Moon's primordial crust. Dubbed the "Genesis Rock" by journalists, its age has been measured at 4.5 billion years, only 100 million years younger than the solar system itself. On their discovery, an elated Scott declared, "We've found what we came for." In this view, Scott manipulates collection tongs at Spur. Hasselblad 70 mm black-and-white negative by James Irwin, Apollo 15, July 26–August 7, 1971.

77. Broken layers of basalt, once deposited as lava flows, poke out of the dust-covered wall of Hadley Rille. Although geologists had obtained extensive evidence that the lunar seas were composed of layered volcanic flows, Hadley Rille provided the only example of in-situ rock layers visited on the lunar surface. Hasselblad 70mm black-and-white negative made with a 500mm lens by David Scott, Apollo 15, July 26–August 7, 1971.

78. The tiny lunar module *Challenger* seen from almost 2 miles away, photographed with a 500mm lens from the base of the North Massif. The large blocky craters to the right are Camelot and Horatio, while the sides of the South Massif rise steeply 5 miles away in the background. Hasselblad 70 mm black-and-white negative by Eugene Cernan, Apollo 17, December 7–19, 1972.

79. Image composite of mission commander David Scott photographing a geologic find before bagging it, 300 feet up the flank of 11,500-foot-high Hadley Delta mountain. The white spots above him are lens flares caused by shooting directly east into the Sun; the mountains behind him are 10½ miles away. Hasselblad 70mm black-and-white negatives by James Irwin, Apollo 15, July 26–August 7, 1971.

80. A boulder field near the eastern rim of Hadley Rille, with Hadley Delta mountain in the background. Hasselblad 70mm black-and-white negative by James Irwin, Apollo 15, July 26–August 7, 1971.

81. On the slopes of the North Massif, Eugene Cernan and Harrison Schmitt visited a house-sized, five-piece boulder known as "Split Rock" (see captions 84 and 86). The boulder, a portion of which is seen here, is composed of material ejected from the giant impact basin located at the Sea of Serenity. Cernan's arm and leg are seen at right; the South Massif is visible at upper left, beyond the boulder. Hasselblad 70mm black-and-white negative by Harrison Schmitt, Apollo 17, December 7–19, 1972.

82. Geologist-astronaut Harrison Schmitt, the first professional scientist to walk on another world, stands next to the rover at the rim of 360-foot-wide Shorty Crater. It was at Shorty that Schmitt discovered an unusual orange soil, which is visible in subtle patches near the rover and in streaks on the crater walls. At first, Schmitt believed the orange coloration was the result of volcanic gases escaping through cracks in the lunar crust in relatively recent lunar geologic history. However, samples of the rare soil analyzed on Earth proved to be 3.7 billion years old. They consist of microscopic beads of glass, colored by titanium, created by volcanic "fire fountains" that sprayed forth from deep within the Moon's interior. Behind Schmitt, on the horizon almost 4 miles away, Family Mountain rises among the peaks of the Taurus-Littrow mountains. Hasselblad 70mm transparencies by Eugene Cernan, Apollo 17, December 7–19, 1972.

83. Alan Bean placing a double-core tube in the ground at Halo Crater, about to push it in as far as he can before hammering it to full depth. Core samples of the lunar soil were an invaluable method for deciphering its history. Hasselblad 70mm black-and-white negative by Charles Conrad, Apollo 12, November 14–24, 1969.

84. Photographic composite of Eugene Cernan and the rover near Split Rock (see captions 81 and 86). The boulder – now broken into five separate pieces – is a breccia, or rock made of fragments of other rocks, that has rolled down the side of the steep North Massif in a 1,500-foot-long furrow. The Sculptured Hills are visible beyond the boulder, and the South Massif can be seen to the far right. Cernan leans on an instrument called a gravimeter, used to measure variations in the lunar gravity field. Hasselblad 70mm black-and-white negatives by Harrison Schmitt, Apollo 17, December 7–19, 1972.

85. Charles Duke has planted the long-handled scoop in the dust while John Young, at left, stands by holding the geology hammer. Beyond sits the lunar rover. The shadow of Duke's helmet intrudes at lower right to create a simple but beautiful visual composition. Hasselblad 70mm black-and-white negative by Charles Duke, Apollo 16, April 16–27, 1972.

86. Panoramic composite of Harrison Schmitt about to walk behind Split Rock (see captions 81 and 84). Scoop marks in the debris on the side of the boulder mark the location of samples collected by Eugene Cernan. The South Massif is to the right 5 miles away, the East Massif is visible on the left. The lunar module *Challenger*, surrounded by a bright halo of disturbed soil, is just visible in the far distance about an inch to the right of the top point of the boulder. Hasselblad 70mm transparencies by Eugene Cernan, Apollo 17, December 7–19, 1972.

87. A last look out at the valley of Taurus-Littrow from the edge of Split Rock, with the Sculptured Hills in the center background and the flank of the North Massif to the right. A discarded plastic rock sample bag keeps some of Apollo's final footprints company. Hasselblad 70mm black-and-white negative by Harrison Schmitt, Apollo 17, December 7–19, 1972.

88. A close-up of John Young on Stone Mountain changing a film magazine, with the camera storage area under his seat visible to the lower left, and the lunar rover's control stick to the right. Hasselblad 70mm transparency by Charles Duke, Apollo 16, April 16–27, 1972.

89. David Scott stands near his commander's seat at the lunar rover. In the foreground at left is a set of photo maps made from unmanned Lunar Orbiter images; at right is the longhandled soil scoop. A plaque on the side of the rover's instrument console reads "Man's First Wheels on the Moon." Hasselblad 70mm transparency by James Irwin, Apollo 15, July 26–August 7, 1971.

90. Photographic composite of David Scott walking toward Hadley Rille, where he will photograph its far wall (see caption 77) using the 500mm lens visible in his left hand. Hadley Delta mountain in the center and Mount Hadley to the left are both part of the front range of the Apennine Mountains, which rise 15,000 feet above the floor of the Sea of Rains. Hasselblad 70mm black-and-white negatives by James Irwin, Apollo 15, July 26–August 7, 1971.

91. Harrison Schmitt's view of the Moon as he rode in his right-hand seat on the lunar rover. In the foreground is the rover's television camera, which could be remotely controlled from Earth to relay the astronauts' activities to the world. In Houston, Schmitt's scientific colleagues used the camera to monitor Apollo 17's explorations, offering information and advice to the two moonwalkers. Hasselblad 70mm black-and-white negative by Harrison Schmitt, Apollo 17, December 7–19, 1972.

92. The low-gain communications antenna of the rover, seen from lunar module pilot Jim Irwin's seat. Irwin, who had come to love the desert at Edwards Air Force Base in California, later called the Moon the "ultimate desert." Hasselblad 70mm black-and-white negative by James Irwin, Apollo 15, July 26–August 7, 1971.

93. Boulders composed of basaltic rock litter the ground near the south rim of Camelot Crater in this westward-looking view. The large block just right of center is 6 feet high. The boulders were ejected from underlying lava flows by the impact that formed Camelot some 70 million years ago. Hasselblad 70mm transparency by Eugene Cernan, Apollo 17, December 7–19, 1972.

94. Photographic composite of the Taurus-Littrow valley. On the horizon, from left to right, we see the Sculptured Hills, the East Massif rising over geologist-astronaut Harrison Schmitt, Bear Mountain, the 7,500-foot-high South Massif, and finally the North Massif rising almost 7,000 feet over Camelot Crater, itself 2,000 feet in diameter. Hasselblad 70mm transparencies by Eugene Cernan, Apollo 17, December 7–19, 1972.

95. Looking deceptively like a giant dune of soft sand, Mount Hadley rises 15,000 feet over the Marsh of Decay, a vertical rise seen only in a few places on Earth. Rover tracks stretch into the distance, like a lunar version of the Oregon Trail. Hasselblad 70mm black-and-white negative by James Irwin, Apollo 15, July 26–August 7, 1971.

96. Back at the lunar module *Falcon* after three days of exploration, James Irwin photographs the Apennine mountains and the lunar rover through one of *Falcon's* landing legs. In the foreground sits the modular equipment stowage assembly (MESA), which contained geology tools, television camera, and other equipment. Hasselblad 70mm transparency by James Irwin, Apollo 15, July 26–August 7, 1971.

97. The footprints of history's first lunar explorers cover the Sea of Tranquillity, after the moonwalk's conclusion. In a few hours Neil Armstrong and Edwin Aldrin will fire their lander's ascent rocket to return to lunar orbit. Hasselblad 70mm black-and-white negative by Edwin Aldrin, Apollo 11, July 16–24, 1969.

98. The crescent Earth hangs above the lunar module *Antares* near the end of Apollo 14's second moonwalk. Hasselblad 70mm black-and-white negative by Alan Shepard, Apollo 14, January 31–February 9, 1971.

99. Eugene Cernan photographing the shadow of his own space helmet. The glow surrounding the shadow is caused by scattering of sunlight by lunar dust. In part this is due to the fine structure of the surface, which contains miniature towers of dust particles. Each of these towers casts its own shadow, which is hidden from the viewer when looking directly away from the Sun, creating an impression of greater luminosity. Hasselblad 70mm transparency by Eugene Cernan, Apollo 17, December 7–19, 1972.

100. Inside the lunar module *Challenger*, the Apollo 17 moonwalkers have stowed their space suits and helmets in the rear of the cramped cabin. The astronauts will spend the night in their underwear, sleeping on hammocks strung across the cabin. Hasselblad 70mm transparency by Eugene Cernan, Apollo 17, December 7–19, 1972.

101. A tired mission commander Eugene Cernan, grimy with lunar soil from three days of exploring the Moon's Taurus-Littrow valley. On his chest, underneath his longjohns, are two of the sensors that relayed biomedical data to mission control. Hasselblad 70mm transparency by Harrison Schmitt, Apollo 17, December 7–19, 1972.

102. In a spray of rocket exhaust and foil insulation, the ascent stage of lunar module *Orion* lifts off to begin the ride back into lunar orbit. Onboard are John Young and Charles Duke. This image was radioed to Earth from a remote-controlled television camera mounted on the abandoned rover parked nearby. Radiotransmitted video image made by robotic camera, Apollo 16, April 16–27, 1972.

103. The ascent stage of lunar module *Challenger* photographed from command module *America* just before docking. After docking and transfer of equipment and crew to *America*, *Challenger* was jettisoned and deliberately crashed into the Moon to provide data for Apollo seismometers on the lunar surface. Hasselblad 70mm transparency by Ronald Evans, Apollo 17, December 7–19, 1972.

104. A portion of the metal skin of the lunar module *Orion* has buckled from the stresses of liftoff from the Moon; this was not unusual for the ultrathin ($^1/_{250}$-inch-thick) sheets used to cover the lander's frame. This slight damage poses no risk to Apollo 16 astronauts John Young and Charles Duke, who are about to link up with crewmate Kenneth Mattingly in the command module *Casper*. Hasselblad 70mm transparency made 70 miles above the Sea of Fertility by Kenneth Mattingly, Apollo 16, April 16–27, 1972.

105. At 69 miles above the ancient highlands west of Smyth's Sea, the ascent stage of the lunar module *Orion* rises toward its rendezvous with the command module *Casper*. The crater directly below *Orion*, 22 miles across, is called Schubert B. Hasselblad 70mm transparency by Kenneth Mattingly, Apollo 16, April 16–27, 1972.

106. In NASA's dress rehearsal for the lunar landing, the Apollo 10 command module *Charlie Brown* prepares to dock with the lunar module *Snoopy* in lunar orbit. The command module is coated with reflective material to mirror the Sun's heat. About 12 feet in diameter and weighing 12,500 pounds, it had about as much habitable volume as a walk-in closet (see caption 5). Hasselblad 70mm transparency by Eugene Cernan, Apollo 10, May 18–26, 1969.

107. A slender crescent Earth rises over the lunar highlands in this composite of two images made at an altitude of 70 miles. The steep slopes of the southwestern inner rim of Humboldt Crater are visible towards the left edge of the horizon. Hasselblad 70mm transparency by Alfred Worden, Apollo 15, July 26–August 7, 1971.

108. During their trip home, the Apollo 12 astronauts became the first people to witness an eclipse of the Sun by the Earth, here photographed shortly before atmospheric reentry. Hasselblad 70mm black-and-white negative probably by Richard Gordon, Apollo 12, November 14–24, 1969.

109. A view of the Moon never seen before the space age, captured at about 1,000 miles as the astronauts began their trip back to Earth. The image is centered on the boundary between the lunar nearside and the Moon's hidden face. Three lunar seas are visible as dark patches, clockwise from upper left: the Sea of Crises, the Border Sea, and Smyth's Sea. At lower right are the highlands of the lunar farside. Metric mapping camera black-and-white negative by Kenneth Mattingly, Apollo 16, April 16–27 1972.

110. A distant Earth seen through the window of the lunar module *Aquarius* during Apollo 13's long and arduous return voyage. After the explosion of an oxygen tank rendered the command module *Odyssey* useless, the astronauts used *Aquarius* as a lifeboat. The astronauts spent days in the darkened cabin, with all non-essential systems shut down to save electrical power (see caption 20). Hasselblad 70mm transparency probably by John Swigert, Apollo 13, April 11–17, 1970.

111. The shiny metal skin of the Apollo 10 lunar module *Snoopy* is seen from the command module *Charlie Brown*, which is docked to *Snoopy*'s roof. At center is the lunar module's overhead window, used by the commander during rendezvous maneuvers. The grid marks on the window are used by the commander to judge the relative orientation of the command module and lunar module as he closes in. Hasselblad 70mm transparency by John Young, Apollo 10, May 18–26, 1969.

112. Earth, seen beyond the lunar module *Eagle*, photographed from the command module *Columbia* as the joined craft sped moonward. A set of the lunar module's maneuvering thrusters is seen at top; part of the craft's circular docking target is visible at bottom. Hasselblad 70mm transparency probably by Michael Collins, Apollo 11, July 16–24, 1969.

113. The hatch window of command module *Yankee Clipper*; the condensation inside the glass window was due to a design flaw that was corrected on later flights. Hasselblad 70mm transparency by Richard Gordon, Apollo 12, November 14–24, 1969.

114. For the first time on any Apollo flight, the Apollo 17 astronauts viewed a full Earth as they began their lunar journey. Africa and the Arabian peninsula are clearly visible. The African rain forests are hidden by clouds; the Sahara Desert to the north and Kalahari to the south are clear. It is late spring in the southern hemisphere, and the Antarctic icecap is seen in full sunlight. Hasselblad 70mm transparency by Harrison Schmitt, Apollo 17, December 7–19, 1972.

115. Walter Cunningham sleeps inside the command module in Earth orbit. Hasselblad 70mm transparency by Walter Schirra, Apollo 7, October 11–22, 1968.

116. A half-Earth gleams in the blackness of space as Apollo 13 heads for the Moon. Clouds hide much of North America, but the southwestern United States and part of Mexico are clearly visible. Hasselblad 70mm transparency probably by John Swigert, Apollo 13, April 11–17, 1970.

117. The Apollo 16 astronauts enjoyed this spectacular view of "the blue planet" shortly after leaving Earth orbit. Much of the United States is visible; note the contrast between the arid lands of the American west and the greener regions to the east. The solid white area to the upper left is the Arctic ice cap, with snow-covered terrain below in Canada. Hasselblad 70mm transparency probably by Kenneth Mattingly, Apollo 16, April 16–27, 1972.

118. On board the unmanned Apollo 4 command module, an automatic camera snapped this view of the crescent Earth looking west over the Atlantic from a distance of about 10,000 miles. Apollo 4, the first test flight of the Saturn V Moon rocket, also tested the command module's heatshield in a high-speed reentry similar to those that would be experienced on lunar missions. Automatic Hasselblad transparency, Apollo 4 (unmanned), November 9, 1967.

119. The orange hues of the Horn of Africa contrast with the deep blues of the Earth's oceans in this view made shortly after the translunar injection maneuver. Hasselblad 70mm transparency by Harrison Schmitt, Apollo 17, December 7–19, 1972.

120. Mexico fills this view by the Moon-bound astronauts, showing the eastern and western Sierra Madre mountain ranges. Hasselblad 70mm transparency by Michael Collins, Apollo 11, July 16–24, 1969.

121. The far limb of Earth photographed just before atmospheric reentry, showing late afternoon, sunset and night over Africa. Hasselblad 70mm transparency by Michael Collins, Apollo 11, July 16–24, 1969.

122. The Sahara Desert seen from an orbital altitude of 200 miles, showing the circular Libyan feature Idehan Marzuq. The dune formations of the irregular sandy area to its left are known as Idehan Ubari. Hasselblad 70mm transparency by Richard Gordon, Gemini 11, September 12–15, 1966.

123. Stratocumulus cloud formations over the Pacific Ocean, seen from an altitude of approximately 120 miles. Hasselblad 70mm transparency probably by James McDivitt, Gemini 4, June 3–7, 1965.

124. Clouds at sunset, looking southwest over the Andes from northern Bolivia, Chile and Argentina. Hasselblad 70mm transparency by James Lovell, Gemini 7, December 4–18, 1965.

125. The three main parachutes just upon opening after reentry at an altitude of 10,000 feet, photographed looking straight upward from the command module rendezvous window. Hasselblad 70mm transparency probably by Alan Bean, Skylab 3, July 28–September 25, 1973.

126. The Pacific Ocean seen through the command module window shortly after splashdown, 230 miles southwest of San Diego, California. Hasselblad 70mm transparency probably by Alan Bean, Skylab 3, July 28–September 25, 1973.

127. An image of the full Moon seen from Earth, showing the Apollo landing sites: Apollo 11's Sea of Tranquillity, 12's Ocean of Storms, 14's Fra Mauro Highlands, 15's Hadley-Apennine region, 16's Descartes Highlands, and 17's Taurus-Littrow Valley. 36-inch telescopic photograph made at Lick Observatory, University of California, Santa Cruz, California.

128. Bombarded by meteorites for billions of years, the Moon's surface is pockmarked by craters ranging in size from microscopic pits to giant basins hundreds of miles across. Seen here is a crater measuring only a few inches in diameter. Today the Moon endures far fewer (and smaller) impacts than it did during the solar system's early history. Hasselblad 70mm negative by James Irwin, Apollo 15, July 26–August 7, 1971.

ACKNOWLEDGMENTS

This project would not have happened without the sustained and generous help of many, many people from vastly different fields and worlds. Perhaps my largest debt, however, is to the Apollo photographic archive itself, and to the astronauts who so dedicatedly recorded their missions. Right behind them are the hundreds of thousands of individuals who worked in the Apollo program and made the missions such a resounding success.

At NASA's Lyndon B. Johnson Manned Spacecraft Center in Houston, I owe a special thanks to Image Repositories Supervisor Gary Seloff and his dedicated staff of Linda Fisk and Irene Jenkins, who not only bore with the exacting demands of my image selection for months on end but made me feel warmly at home in their concrete bunker full of film. Mike Gentry and Mary-Louise Schmid did the same for me next door in the Public Affairs Library, adding their own special twist of humor. Michael McGuyer, Carlos Fontanot, and Steve Nesbitt in External Affairs, along with Rick Slater in Photography, cleared the bureaucratic path for digital scanning of the images. Chuck Welch and Sue Runco at JSC answered obscure questions about various images. Equally central thanks go to JSC's Houston neighbor The Lunar and Planetary Institute, where Head of Information and Research Services Mary Ann Hager and Photographer Debra Rueb repeatedly made their treasures and time available to me. LPI's Walter Kiefer, Jack Sevir, and Mary Noell were also helpful in lending their expertise. Tina Pauro, Librarian at the Regional Planetary Image Facility at NASA/Caltech's Jet Propulsion Laboratory in Pasadena, California, made her images and advice available in the early stages of research, as did Robert Tice, Photographic Supervisor at NASA's Goddard Spaceflight Center, Greenbelt, Maryland. Althea Washington and her staff at the NASA Broadcast and Imaging Branch in Washington, D.C., fulfilled lengthy image requests early on, and Rosemary Steinat, Librarian of the RPIF at the Smithsonian's National Air and Space Museum in Washington, D.C., provided crucial laser discs of archive imagery. Among the Apollo astronauts, the enthusiasm and support of Eugene Cernan, David Scott, Russell Schweickart, and Walter Cunningham have been invaluable. Andy Chaikin, author of the definitive 1994 Apollo history, *A Man on the Moon*, has been a complete joy to work with. The generosity with which he applied his encyclopedic Apollo knowledge to the project, especially when it came to the image captions, will always be appreciated. Finally, I would like to thank Eric Jones, author of the masterfully compiled and annotated *Apollo Lunar Surface Journal* (published on the World Wide Web), whose general advice and advocacy of the project throughout the Apollo community opened many doors.

On the production side back in San Francisco, no person was more helpful in the early stages of this project than Kevin Kelly, author of *The Home Planet* (1988), a beautiful and definitive book of Earth-oriented space photography. By sharing hard-won knowledge of both the publishing and space worlds, Kevin opened the doors that made the digital aspect of this project possible, and for this I am forever grateful. Almost as invaluable was John Zax of LotusColor, who cheerfully toiled beyond any call of normal duty or reason for several months to scan about 2000 images on his drum scanner. Alexi Botkin was his able assistant, and both have become friends and trusted digital advisors. Many thanks to Jim Peck of J.P. Digital Imaging in Mountain View, California, who made his Lightjet 5000 direct-digital printer available to the project and learned just how demanding artists can be, but truly exceptional and enduring gratitude goes to Jim's master digital printer Chris Tucker, who shepherded this project as if it were his own child for more than a year. Nearest to ground zero are the talented studio assistants that have worked with me over the years: Michael Rauner, Laura Heyman, Valerie Imus, and Analucia Da Silva all tirelessly allowed me to become the proverbial eight-armed octopus. Thank you. Mark Mardon ably helped in wading through every word of the *Apollo Lunar Surface Journal*, and Jay Berry came to the rescue when I was drowning in the deep cold waters of panorama assembly. A special thanks to master digital imagist Steven Johnson, who offered his seasoned opinions early on, and to the Headlands Center for the Arts in Sausalito, California, which provided me with a room with a view for the book's final edit and sequencing. Illustrator Davi Grossman of Madcat Media in San Francisco created the book's Apollo